Target
Get back on track > 5

Edexcel GCSE (9–1)
History

Medicine through time, c1250–present

Laura Goodyear

Pearson

Published by Pearson Education Limited, 80 Strand, London, WC2R 0RL.

www.pearsonschoolsandfecolleges.co.uk

Copies of official specifications for all Pearson qualifications may be found on the website: qualifications.pearson.com

Text © Pearson Education Limited 2018
Produced by Out of House Publishing Solutions
Typeset by Newgen KnowledgeWorks Pvt. Ltd., Chennai, India

The right of Laura Goodyear to be identified as author of this work has been asserted by her in accordance with the Copyright, Designs and Patents Act 1988.

First published 2018

21 20 19 18
10 9 8 7 6 5 4 3 2

British Library Cataloguing in Publication Data
A catalogue record for this book is available from the British Library

ISBN 978 0 435 189488

Printed in Slovakia by Neografia

Acknowledgements
The authors and publisher would like to thank the following individuals and organisations for their kind permission to reproduce copyright material.

Photographs
(Key: b-bottom; c-centre; l-left; r-right; t-top)

Alamy Stock Photo: Lebrecht Music and Arts Photo Library 29;
Mary Evans Picture Library: Illustrated London News Ltd 11, 12, 19, Pump Park Photography 17, John Maclellan 25

All other images © Pearson Education

Note from the publisher
Pearson has robust editorial processes, including answer and fact checks, to ensure the accuracy of the content in this publication, and every effort is made to ensure this publication is free of errors. We are, however, only human, and occasionally errors do occur. Pearson is not liable for any misunderstandings that arise as a result of errors in this publication, but it is our priority to ensure that the content is accurate. If you spot an error, please do contact us at resourcescorrections@pearson.com so we can make sure it is corrected.

Contents

1 Selecting and applying your own knowledge

Get started		1
The Western Front		3
1	How do I identify relevant features?	5
2	How do I add relevant detail?	6
3	How do I know how much to write?	7
Sample response		8
Your turn!		9
Review your skills		10

2 Following up a source

Get started		11
Medicine on the Western Front		13
1	How do I identify details in the source?	15
2	How do I ask good questions about the source?	16
3	How do I select valid methods of answering my question?	17
Sample response		18
Your turn!		19
Review your skills		20

3 Source provenance, usefulness and reliability

Get started		21
Medicine on the Western Front		23
1	How do I identify what is useful to an historian?	25
2	How do I identify the limitations of a source?	26
3	How do I include judgements about the provenance of the source?	27
Sample response		28
Your turn!		29
Review your skills		30

4 Answering relevantly

Get started		31
Causes of disease		33
1	How do I read the question?	35
2	How do I identify relevant detail?	36
3	How do I plan my answer to ensure it answers the question?	37
Sample response		38
Your turn!		39
Review your skills		40

5 Selecting and using supporting evidence

Get started		41
Medieval ideas on the causes of disease		43
1	How do I select information to answer the question?	45
2	How do I ensure that information is relevant to the concept focus?	46
3	How do I use information of my own?	47
Sample response		48
Your turn!		49
Review your skills		50

6 Understanding change

Get started		51
Changes in medicine, c1700–c1900		53
1	How do I know what makes a change historically significant?	55
2	How do I distinguish between change and continuity?	56
3	How do I decide how significant a change is?	57
Sample response		58
Your turn!		59
Review your skills		60

7 Making links between points

Get started		61
Changes in surgical treatments, c1700–c1900		63
1	How do I know when to use linking phrases?	65
2	How do I make links to develop my supporting knowledge?	66
3	How do I link my ideas and supporting detail back to the question?	67
Sample response		68
Your turn!		69
Review your skills		70

8 Making a judgement

Get started		71
The fight against disease		73
1	How do I organise information to reach a judgement?	75
2	How do I make judgements?	76
3	How do I make a 'good' judgement?	77
Sample response		78
Your turn!		79
Review your skills		80

Answers	81

① Selecting and applying your own knowledge

This unit will help you to identify relevant features of a topic and build on these features with details from your own knowledge. The skills you will build are to:

- choose historical knowledge based on what the question is asking you
- decide how much of your own historical knowledge you need to include in an answer
- use your own historical knowledge effectively.

The skill of selecting and applying your own knowledge is important for all the questions you might be asked in your History GCSE.

In the exam, you will also be asked to tackle questions such as the one below. This unit will prepare you to write your own response to this exam-style question:

Exam-style question

Describe **two** features of the quarries at Arras.

Feature 1

....

....

Feature 2

....

....

(4 marks)

The three key questions in the **skills boosts** will help you to decide what historical knowledge you need when you are answering Paper 1 history questions.

① How do I identify relevant features?

② How do I add relevant detail?

③ How do I know how much to write?

Look at the student response to the exam-style question below:

Exam-style question

Describe **two** features of the quarries at Arras.

During the battle for Arras the British and Commonwealth troops used the existing Roman quarries to launch a surprise attack on the Germans. This meant there was less work to prepare the position of attack and less chance of soldiers being injured through collapse. The quarries also open up into large caverns where the chalk was removed from the ground to be used during the Middle Ages. This meant that soldiers were not confined in cramped conditions and there was even space for a fully functioning hospital where soldiers could be treated and operated on quickly after injury. The quicker a wounded soldier could be treated the more chance they had of survival.

(**1**) Highlight 🖉 any features the student has identified.

(**2**) Cross out ⟨cat⟩ the information in the student answer that is not necessary to answer the question.

(**3**) For each feature identified the student gives one extra detail to expand the information. Try to identify 🖉 this extra detail for each feature.

Feature 1 ....

....

....

Feature 2 ....

....

....

The Western Front

This unit uses the theme of the Western Front to build your skills in selecting and applying your own knowledge. If you need to review your knowledge of this theme, work through these pages.

(1) Read the statements about the Western Front below and tick ✓ the two correct ones.

a The Western Front stretched from France in the north to Germany in the south.

b Both sides were focused on **defending** the land they held by the end of 1914.

c Fighting on the Western Front began in 1915.

d By the end of the war, the line of the Western Front had barely moved.

(2) Label ✐ each feature in the diagram of a trench system below, using the words provided in the list.

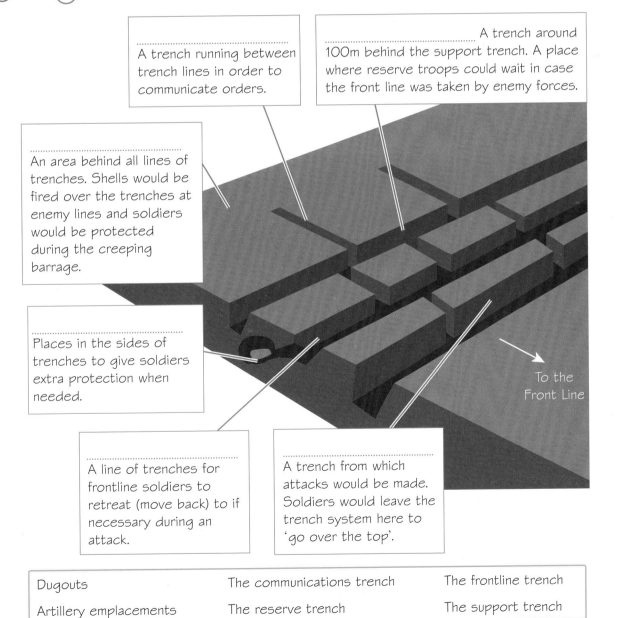

.... A trench running between trench lines in order to communicate orders.

.... A trench around 100m behind the support trench. A place where reserve troops could wait in case the front line was taken by enemy forces.

.... An area behind all lines of trenches. Shells would be fired over the trenches at enemy lines and soldiers would be protected during the creeping barrage.

.... Places in the sides of trenches to give soldiers extra protection when needed.

To the Front Line

.... A line of trenches for frontline soldiers to retreat (move back) to if necessary during an attack.

.... A trench from which attacks would be made. Soldiers would leave the trench system here to 'go over the top'.

Dugouts	The communications trench	The frontline trench
Artillery emplacements	The reserve trench	The support trench

③ Circle Ⓐ all the advantages of using ready-dug quarries as opposed to digging new tunnels.

less chance of collapse	soldiers didn't get as scared before the attack
room to create an underground hospital	more hygienic environment
less chance of being heard by the enemy	large, well-ventilated spaces

④ Draw 🖉 lines linking the problem to each method of initially transporting wounded soldiers at the Western Front.

Method of transportation

A Stretcher bearers

B Horses

C Motorised ambulances

Problem

a struggled to cope with the mud and uneven terrain

b were considered too slow to deal with the large numbers of casualties

c were exposed to gunfire and shelling and may be killed or injured themselves

⑤ For each of the conditions below, identify 🖉 the environmental element causing it from the options listed at the bottom of the page.

a **Trench fever** – flu-like symptoms and high temperature.

....

b **Trench foot** – painful swelling of the feet. In second stage, gangrene (the decomposition of flesh) sets in due to a loss of the blood supply to the foot.

....

c **Shell shock** – often not recognised or understood at the time. Caused tiredness, headaches, nightmares, loss of speech, uncontrollable shaking and complete mental breakdown.

....

d **Gas exposure** – effects depended on type of gas but generally caused internal and external irritation, blindness and in some cases death through suffocation.

....

Lice and other pests who lived in trenches	Constantly wet and muddy conditions
Frequent shelling and exposure to danger	Gasses being trapped in trenches below ground level

How do I identify relevant features?

To identify two features so you can answer relevantly you will need to:
- read the question and highlight the topic of Medicine on the Western Front
- make a list of features of this topic from your own knowledge.

Look at the two exam questions below:

A

Exam-style question

Describe **two** features of transportation of wounded soldiers from the Front Line.

Feature 1 ....

....

Feature 2 ....

....

(4 marks)

B

Exam-style question

Describe **two** features of the trench environment which were unhealthy.

Feature 1 ....

....

Feature 2 ....

....

(4 marks)

(1) Highlight ✎ the 'topic' parts of questions A and B.

(2) (a) The text you have highlighted in the exam-style questions above tells you what knowledge to use to describe **relevant** features. Look at the features described below and sort them into the table under the correct heading. ✎

Question A	Question B

Horses were used to transport wounded soldiers to CCSs.

Trenches were often saturated by rain and very muddy or filled with water.

Pests such as lice and rats were a common problem, infesting the trenches and men's uniforms.

Stretcher bearers collected the wounded men from no-man's-land.

(b) Add ✎ one more feature for each question.

② How do I add relevant detail?

It is necessary to support the feature you have identified with relevant details to develop your answer.

① The table below shows each of the features identified for the two exam-style questions on the previous page. Draw ✏️ lines linking the feature to its supporting detail.

Feature	Supporting detail

A Horses were used to transport wounded soldiers to CCSs.

a It was only possible to collect the wounded from no-man's-land using men carrying stretchers but they had to perform their duties under very dangerous conditions and risked becoming wounded themselves.

B Stretcher bearers collected the wounded men from no-man's-land.

b It was discovered that the lice carried a disease that caused the soldiers to suffer from flu-like symptoms. This illness was called trench fever.

C Trenches were often saturated by rain and very muddy or filled with water.

c Although they were considered too slow and struggled to cope with the large numbers of wounded soldiers, they did not break down in the muddy conditions so continued to be used.

D Pests such as lice and rats were a common problem, infesting the trenches and men's uniforms.

d This often caused a condition called trench foot, which is when the blood supply to the foot is lost and the skin begins to decompose.

② Now write ✏️ the two features you added of your own in ② ⓑ of page 5 and add a supporting detail to each to develop your description.

My feature	Supporting detail
Exam-style question A:	
Exam-style question B:	

3 How do I know how much to write?

Question 1 is worth just 4 marks, so each relevant feature you identify will score a mark and each relevant supporting detail will score a mark. This means full marks can be achieved with just four sentences.

(1) You are now going to use the relevant features and the details that have been identified to practise writing an answer to the following exam-style questions. Fill in the tables to help you to see what you need to write for each answer.

Question A:

> **Exam-style question**
>
> Describe **two** features of transportation of wounded soldiers from the Front Line.

Sentence 1 (feature 1)	
Sentence 2 (supporting detail)	
Sentence 3 (feature 2)	
Sentence 4 (supporting detail)	

Question B:

> **Exam-style question**
>
> Describe **two** features of the trench environment which were unhealthy.

Sentence 1 (feature 1)	
Sentence 2 (supporting detail)	
Sentence 3 (feature 2)	
Sentence 4 (supporting detail)	

Sample response

Read the exam-style question below and the student response that follows.

Exam-style question

Describe **two** features of the support trench system.

Feature 1 ....

....

....

....

Feature 2 ....

....

....

....

(4 marks)

The support trenches were about 80 metres behind the frontline trenches. They were where additional men and supplies could be kept in case of an attack on the front line. The communication trenches ran between the lines of trenches to allow messages and supplies to be transported backwards and forwards between the lines. Conditions were safer in the support trenches than the front line as they were not within range of enemy snipers.

/4

(1) Annotate the answer highlighting 🖉 one feature and its supporting detail in one colour and the second feature and its supporting detail in another. To help you could write 🖉 the answer into the exam-style question.

(2) Give the answer a score out of 4. 🖉

(3) Circle (A) and label 🖉 the feature which is not relevant.

(4) Write 🖉 an additional feature that might be more relevant to this question. How would you support it?

Feature: ....

....

Supporting detail: ....

....

....

Your turn!

Now it is your turn to try to answer an exam-style question.

Exam-style question

Describe **two** features of the dugout.

(**1**) Highlight ✎ the topic from which you must select your features.

(**2**) List ✎ two features relevant to this topic.

1 ....

....

2 ....

....

(**3**) Use the table below to plan ✎ a relevant detail to support each feature.

1	
2	

(**4**) Now write ✎ your answer as a descriptive paragraph of four sentences.

Feature 1

....

....

Supporting detail

....

....

....

Feature 2

....

....

Supporting detail

....

....

....

Review your skills

Check up

Review your response to the exam-style question on page 9. Tick ✓ the column below to show how well you think you have done each of the following.

	Had a go ✓	Nearly there ✓	Got it! ✓
identified the 'topic' in the question to ensure features are relevant	☐	☐	☐
selected two features and added relevant detail	☐	☐	☐
worked out how much to write	☐	☐	☐

Need more practice?

If you want to practise another exam-style question, have a go ✏ at the one below.

Exam-style question

Describe **two** features of the environment at the Front Line.

Feature 1 ....

....

....

....

Feature 2 ....

....

....

....

(4 marks)

How confident do you feel about each of these **skills**? Colour ✏ in the bars.

1 How do I identify relevant features?	2 How do I add relevant detail?	3 How do I know how much to write?
☐☐☐☐	☐☐☐☐	☐☐☐☐

② Following up a source

This unit will help you learn and practise how to select intriguing details from a source, and then plan a follow-up enquiry around it.

The skills you will build are to:

- select details from sources that could be followed up
- ask questions about source details
- suggest valid methods of answering your questions.

In the exam, you will also be asked to tackle questions such as the one below. This unit will prepare you to write your own response to this exam-style question.

Exam-style question

Study Source A.

How could you follow up Source A to find out more about medical treatment on the Western Front?

In your answer, you must give the question you would ask and the type of source you could use.

Complete the table below.

(4 marks)

Detail in Source A that I would follow up: ....

Question I would ask: ....

What type of source I could use: ....

How this might help answer my question: ....

Source A | *RAMC officers posing in front of a mobile bacteriological laboratory in France in 1915.*

Notice the types of questions you are being asked in this question.

? What detail would I follow up on?

? What further questions would I ask?

? What type of source could I use to answer these?

? How might this answer my question?

The three key questions in the **skills boosts** will help you answer the four questions above.

1 How do I identify details in the source?

2 How do I ask good questions about the source?

3 How do I select valid methods of answering my question?

Here are some questions you might consider when looking at Source A.

1 | **What aspect of medicine is being demonstrated?** This source is a photograph of a RAMC vehicle – a mobile bacteriological laboratory, therefore it is telling us about services provided by the RAMC and a bit about how wound infection and other diseases were dealt with on the Western Front.

4 | **What is the provenance?** This tells us a bit about the source, ideally who produced it, and when and where it was produced. When the source is a photograph or picture, it may provide you with a little more detail about what you are looking at.

Source A | *RAMC officers posing in front of a mobile bacteriological laboratory in France in 1915.*

2 | **What question(s) do you still have about this aspect of medicine?**
For example, you might want to know what else the RAMC did; how infections and diseases were treated once identified; how many of these vehicles there were; how many deaths they prevented.
Can you think of any other relevant questions for this source?

3 | **Where might you find further evidence?** Government data and statistics; medical records; doctors' and nurses' diaries; soldiers' letters home; newspaper articles; expert accounts, etc.

① a Write down 🖉 one of the questions you would like to ask to follow up this source.

....

....

....

....

b Note down 🖉 what type of source you think is most likely to answer your question.

....

....

....

....

c Why do you think this is most likely to provide you with an answer? 🖉

....

....

....

....

Medicine on the Western Front

This unit uses the theme of Medicine on the Western Front to build your skills in following up a source. If you need to review your knowledge of this theme, work through these pages.

The Royal Army Medical Corps (RAMC) was responsible for medical care on the Western Front. First Aid Nursing Yeomanry (FANY) was the first women's voluntary organisation to send volunteers to the Western Front.

1 In the table below:

a Highlight ✐ two roles played by the RAMC on the Western Front.

b Circle Ⓐ two roles played by the FANY on the Western Front.

Medical officers	Medical orderlies	Providing baths with heated water via vans	Setting up cinemas
Driving food supplies and clothing to the Front Line	Stretcher bearers	Driving patients in ambulance wagons	Overseeing all stages of casualty evacuation

2 The information below shows the chain of evacuation of injured troops from the Front but the descriptions have been jumbled up.

a Write ✐ a number from 1–4 in the box under each stage in order to demonstrate the theoretical chain of evacuation (note however that this order often changed, depending on the nature of the casualty).

b Now link ✐ the terms in the left-hand column to their correct descriptions in the right-hand column.

A Regimental Aid Post (RAP)	**a** Located near the French and Belgian coast, so that wounded men who were treated there would be close to the ports from which they could be transported home to Britain.
B Base hospitals	**b** These were set up in buildings such as factories or schools, often near a railway to allow the next stage of the chain of evacuation to take place quickly. Those closest to the Front Line would specialise in operating on the most critical injuries, such as those to the chest. Soldiers arriving here would be triaged to decide the severity of their wounds.
C Advanced and main dressing stations	**c** Generally located within 200m of the Front Line, in communication trenches or deserted buildings, these were staffed by a Regimental Medical Officer, plus some stretcher bearers with first-aid knowledge. Their purpose was to administer immediate first aid and get as many men back to the fighting as possible. Wounded men would either walk in or be carried in by other soldiers.
D Casualty clearing stations	**d** Where possible, these were about 400m from the RAP in abandoned buildings, dugouts or bunkers, in order to offer protection from enemy shelling. Where these were not available, tents were used. Wounded men would walk there if they were able, or would be carried on stretchers in stages.

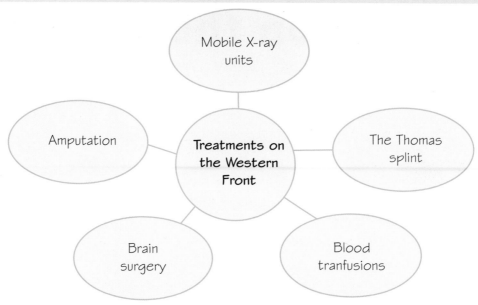

(3) On the diagram above:

(a) Highlight 🖊 treatments that could be used to treat a shrapnel wound.

(b) Underline (A) the treatment used to treat shock.

(c) Circle (A) the treatment used to treat brain injury.

(d) Highlight 🖊 in another colour the treatment used to treat infection.

(4) (a) On the table below, highlight 🖊 the problems and solutions to do with mobile X-ray units in one colour and the problems and solutions to do with blood transfusions in another. Use the colour code key to mark your colours.

Colour code: Mobile X-ray units [   ]   Blood transfusions [   ]

Problems	Attempted solutions
Extremely fragile imaging equipment was difficult to move.	It was known that type O blood was a universal donor which could safely be given to anyone.
Difficult to keep blood fresh when transporting it to patients, as it could not be refrigerated.	Adding sodium citrate to donated blood prevented clotting and meant it could be stored for longer.
Images did not detect certain materials or debris in wounds, such as fragments of clothing, which could cause infection if not removed.	Units were set up in tents next to the van which carried the fragile imaging equipment.
If a patient was given the wrong blood type, they might suffer a serious reaction.	Mobile units were only used for emergency detection of shrapnel. Better-quality images could be taken at base hospitals.

(b) Now link 🖊 the solutions so they match the problem they solve.

How do I identify details in the source?

In order to start following up a source for an enquiry, you need to understand what the source is about and identify relevant details.

Look at the exam-style question and source below.

Exam-style question

How could you follow up Source B to find out more about the problems involved in performing operations on the Western Front?

In your answer, you must give the question you would ask and the type of source you could use.

Source B *From the diary of Oswald Roberston, written on 30 November 1917. He was an army surgeon working on the Western Front during the First World War.*

Men were horribly mutilated – many were dying when brought into the ward. All the beds were full and we began putting stretchers on the floor. Blood everywhere – clothes soaked in blood, pools of blood in the stretchers, streams of blood dropping from the stretchers to the floor. My rubber apron was one solid red smear. All we could do was try to stop the bleeding and get the patients as comfortable as possible. I could only transfuse an occasional patient. The majority had to take their chance and go through the operation as best they could.

(1) In the table below, tick ✓ which of the following are aspects of medicine mentioned by the source.

Controlling blood loss ☐

General care (making the patient comfortable) ☐

Performing X-rays ☐

Reducing infection ☐

Bandaging wounds ☐

Blood transfusions ☐

Operating ☐

(2) Note down 🖉 **one** of the sections you have ticked that could be described as 'a problem involved in performing operations on the Western Front'.

....

You must select just one detail from the source for this exam question, so select the relevant detail you feel most confident to follow up.

(3) Write down 🖉 why you chose this detail.

....

....

....

....

2 How do I ask good questions about the source?

Historians will always use as many sources as possible because every source has its own strengths and weaknesses. Considering these strengths and weaknesses will help you to ask good questions when following up a source.

Look at this exam-style question and source below.

Exam-style question

How could you follow up Source C to find out more about the problems involved in caring for casualties on the Western Front?

In your answer, you must give the question you would ask and the type of source you could use.

Source C From an account by Reverend Leonard Pearson, written in 1916. He was the army chaplain at Casualty Clearing Station 44 during the Battle of the Somme (1916).

I spent most of my time giving anaesthetics. I had no right to be doing this because I had no medical qualifications, but we were simply so rushed. We couldn't get the wounded into the hospital quickly enough and the journey from the battlefield was simply terrible for these poor lads. It was a question of operating as quickly as possible. If they had to wait their turn in the normal way, until the surgeon was able to perform the operation with a doctor giving the anaesthetic, it would have been too late for many of them. As it was, many died. We all simply had to help and do anything that was needed.

| Anaesthetics | Surgery | Untrained medical staff | Pain | Evacuation process |

(1) Circle (A) all the aspects of medicine mentioned in the source and link them (✎) to the correct label.

(2) (a) Write (✎) a detail from Source C that you would like to follow up.

....

....

(b) For the detail you have chosen, write (✎) **three** questions using the starters below in order to explore it further:

Why ....

How ....

Where ....

(c) Which of your three questions above would you choose to follow up the source and why? (✎)

....

....

....

....

3 How do I select valid methods of answering my question?

When answering a question that requires you to follow up on a source, you must select a source to help you answer the question you have set yourself.

Look at the exam-style question and related source below.

Exam-style question

How could you follow up Source D to find out more about the problems involved in treating wounded soldiers on the Western Front?

In your answer, you must give the question you would ask and the type of source you could use.

Source D *A British casualty clearing station, Western Front, circa 1916*

1. Underline (A) the section of the exam-style question that identifies the aspect of medicine being discussed.

2. Write down one new question of your own, related to a detail in the source.

....

3. a Look at the suggested sources in the table below. Write notes on how useful each one is likely to be for the question you wrote in (2).

Source	Suggested usefulness of source	
A photograph of an operating theatre		
A statistical source about mortality (death) rates on the Western Front		
An account of his experience by an injured soldier		
An account of an operation by a military surgeon		
A politician's speech about government spending of military money		

b In the last column, tick ✓ the source you think would be most useful in answering your own new question from (2).

c Explain how the type of source you have chosen could help you answer your own new question from (2).

> *Source:* ....
>
> *I believe this will be able to answer my question because:* ....
>
> ....
>
> ....

Sample response

Read the source, exam-style question and student answer below.

Source E *From an account by Reverend Leonard Pearson, written in 1916. He was the army chaplain at Casualty Clearing Station 44 during the Battle of the Somme (1916).*

I spent most of my time giving anaesthetics. I had no right to be doing this because I had no medical qualifications, but we were simply so rushed. We couldn't get the wounded into the hospital quickly enough and the journey from the battlefield was simply terrible for these poor lads. It was a question of operating as quickly as possible. If they had to wait their turn in the normal way, until the surgeon was able to perform the operation with a doctor giving the anaesthetic, it would have been too late for many of them. As it was, many died. We all simply had to help and do anything that was needed.

Exam-style question

Study Source E.

How could you follow up Source E to find out more about the problems involved in performing operations on the Western Front?

In your answer, you must give the question you would ask and the type of source you could use.

Complete the table below.

(4 marks)

Detail in Source E that I would follow up:
I spent most of my time giving anaesthetics.

Question I would ask:
Why were people with no medical qualifications giving anaesthetics?

What type of source I could use:
A photograph of a Casualty Clearing Station.

How this might help answer my question:
A photograph of a Casualty Clearing Station might show the large numbers of wounded soldiers.

(1) Highlight ✐ the section in the source which outlines the use of anaesthetics on the Western Front.

(2) Note down ✐ how you might improve the question this student asks or use your own knowledge to give an alternative question.

....

(3) Can you think of a better source to answer the student's question? Write ✐ your suggestion below.

....

(4) Explain why ✐ you think your source would be better by saying how it might help answer the question.

....

....

Your turn!

Now you are going to write your own answer to this exam-style question.

Study Source A.

How could you follow up Source A to find out more about the treatment of the sick? In your answer you must give the question you would ask and the type of source you could use.

Complete the table below.

(4 marks)

Detail in Source A that I would follow up:

....

....

....

Question I would ask:

....

....

....

What type of source I could use:

....

....

....

How this might help answer my question:

....

....

....

Source A *RAMC officers posing in front of a mobile bacteriological laboratory in France in 1915.*

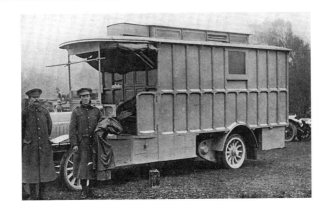

Review your skills

Check up

Review your response to the exam-style question on page 19. Tick ⊘ the column to show how well you think you have done each of the following.

	Had a go ⊘	Nearly there ⊘	Got it! ⊘
identified details in the source	☐	☐	☐
asked a valid question	☐	☐	☐
suggested the usefulness of follow-up sources.	☐	☐	☐

Need more practice?

If you want to practise another exam-style question, try ⊘ this one on paper:

Exam-style question

Study Source A.

How could you follow up Source A to find out more about the speed of treatment on the Western Front?

In your answer, you must give the question you would ask and the type of source you could use.

Complete the table below.

(4 marks)

Detail in Source A that I would follow up:

....

Question I would ask:

....

What type of source I could use:

....

How this might help answer my question:

....

How confident do you feel about each of these **skills**? Colour ⊘ in the bars.

1 How do I identify details in the source?

2 How do I ask good questions about the source?

3 How do I select valid methods of answering my question?

③ Source provenance, usefulness and reliability

This unit will help you to decide how useful a source is. The skills you will build are to:

- choose details from a source based on what is useful for investigating a given topic
- recognise the limitations of sources in finding out what you need to know
- make judgements about the provenance of a source to help your explanation.

In the exam, you will also be asked to tackle questions such as the one below. This unit will prepare you to write your own response to this question.

Exam-style question

Study Sources A and B on page 25.

How useful are Sources A and B for an enquiry into the treatments for shrapnel wounds?

Explain your answer, using Sources A and B and your knowledge of the historical context.   **(8 marks)**

As you read a source, ask yourself the following questions:

? Who made / wrote it?

? What details might not be useful?

? Why might it not be reliable?

? Why was it made / written?

? Is this type of source useful to me to answer my questions?

? What details might be useful?

The three key questions in the **skills boosts** will help you to analyse and evaluate a source to decide how useful it is.

① How do I identify what is useful to an historian?

② How do I identify the limitations of a source?

③ How do I include judgements about the provenance of the source?

Look at the extract student response to the following exam-style question. It is a source utility question. This extract covers how useful the student thinks Source C is.

Exam-style question

How useful are Sources C and D for an enquiry into the effects of poison gas attacks?

Explain your answer, using Sources C and D and your knowledge of the historical context.

Source C *From the notebook of Lance Sergeant Elmer Cotton, who served in the 5th Northumberland Fusiliers in 1915. He is describing the effects of a chlorine gas attack.*

It produces a flooding of the lungs. It is the equivalent to drowning, only on dry land. The effects are these – a splitting headache and a terrific thirst (but to drink is instant death), a knife-edge pain in the lungs and the coughing up of a greenish froth off the stomach and the lungs, finally resulting in death. It is a fiendish death to die.

Source C is useful, as it tells the historian about the effect of chlorine gas on someone who has been exposed. It describes the effect on the lungs as like drowning, which is because chlorine gas caused irritation that led to fluid building up in the lungs and possible suffocation. It also describes symptoms such as headaches and chest pain. We can assume that, as a soldier writing about the effects of gas, he had first-hand experience of witnessing these symptoms and the fact that these are notes taken at the time make this account more useful to the historian, as he is describing what he is seeing rather than remembering these facts. Though Cotton speaks about cases he has witnessed, it's unclear whether these symptoms, followed by death, were typical of all soldiers exposed to chlorine gas. Also the provenance does not say that Lance Sergeant Elmer Cotton had any medical training, which may mean he is less able to accurately identify medical symptoms.

(1) Read the student response and then do the following:

 (a) Highlight 🖊 in one colour details about the source that they find useful.

 (b) Highlight 🖊 in another colour where they have discussed the limitations of the source.

 (c) Circle Ⓐ any text using or questioning the impact of the provenance of the source.

 (d) Underline Ⓐ any text where the student has used their own knowledge to explain how the source is useful or its limitations.

Medicine on the Western Front

This unit uses the theme of Medicine on the Western Front to build your skills in assessing the utility of a source. If you need to review your knowledge of this theme, work through these pages.

1 When a shell exploded it sent bits of metal flying, causing injury to soldiers. What were these fragments of metal commonly known as? Tick (✓) your choice.

a bullets ☐   **b** shell fragments ☐   **c** shrapnel ☐

2 Read the following extract taken from an interview in 1974 with Captain Maberly Esler who was a medical officer at Hooge, in the Ypres salient, in June 1915.

> In our frontline dugout we had first aid **dressing** and morphia [**morphine**] and that was all. We'd never attempt any major surgery or anything like that in the trenches – one couldn't do it. The only thing you could do was to cover a wound to keep it from getting infected, or stop a haemorrhage by compression if they were bleeding to death.
>
> Several people got **tetanus** afterwards from an infection in the ground which was carried in shelled areas. The ground had been shelled for such a long time it was in rather a **septic** sort of condition.

a From the context of the extract, describe 🖉 the following terms:

   i morphine ....

   ii haemorrhage ....

   iii dressing ....

   iv tetanus ....

   v septic ....

b What does Captain Esler identify as the most significant problem of wounds, especially those caused by shrapnel? 🖉

....

3 Read the descriptions of effective wound and injury preventions during the First World War.

The Brodie helmet was introduced in 1915. This was a steel helmet with a strap that prevented it being thrown off the head in an explosion.	'Gas gangrene', which could be caused by bacteria in the soil, could affect wounds and spread rapidly. Infected limbs could be amputated.
The impact of tetanus was reduced by the use of anti-tetanus injections from the end of 1914.	In the late 19th century, Hugh Thomas designed a splint to stop joints from moving called the Thomas Splint.

a Highlight 🖉 in one colour actions to prevent the severity of wounds.

b Highlight 🖉 in another colour actions to prevent infection once wounds had happened.

4 Gas was not a major cause of death on the Western Front, in comparison to wounds. However, it caused major panic and fear among soldiers.

a Draw ✎ lines linking the descriptions to the type of gas they are describing.

A Mustard gas	**a** First used at the end of 1915 near Ypres. This gas had similar effects to chlorine gas but worked much faster. Could kill in just a couple of days.
B Chlorine gas	**b** First used by the Germans in 1917. This odourless gas caused internal and external irritation and blisters. It could pass through clothing.
C Phosgene gas	**c** First used by the Germans at the first Battle of Ypres in 1915. This gas was the first to be used and caused suffocation when inhaled. Medical services were not prepared for the use of gas at this stage, so soldiers initially had no gas masks as protection.

b What solution did soldiers find to the initial lack of gas masks? ✎

....

It involved soaking cotton pads in something a soldier always has with them!

5 **a** Below are three other medical issues that soldiers faced. Below each condition, write ✎ a brief description.

b Draw ✎ a line to match the condition to the relevant treatment(s).

There may be more than one treatment for each condition.

A Shell shock	**a** Delousing stations and mobile baths
....	
....	**b** Rubbing oil into feet
....	
B Trench fever	**c** Regularly changing socks
....	
....	**d** Never fully understood
....	
C Trench foot	**e** Amputation as a last resort to prevent spread
....	
....	**f** Time spent in Craiglockhart War Hospital for Officers

How do I identify what is useful to an historian?

To answer a source utility question, you need to identify the details the source is providing that are useful to an historian studying a particular topic, which will be identified in the question. To do this you should:

- identify the topic about Medicine on the Western Front that the question requires you to focus on
- select appropriate details from the source, which help you learn more about this topic.

Source A *From a speech made by Walter Roch in Parliament, 23 June 1915. Roch was a Liberal MP and was taking part in a debate on how the government should spend its money.*

I want to bring to the notice of the House information in connection with the treatment of the wounded in Flanders. The information is not my own personal knowledge, but from several very close personal friends who have been connected with this, although I cannot give their names. I am told that it is of the utmost importance that the men who are wounded should be treated as quickly as possible, and that their wounds should have the best possible attention as soon as may be. The suggestion I have to make is that there should be many more of these evacuation hospitals than there are in France at the present moment, that they should be much better equipped with operating theatres and other appliances, and that they should be more sanitary and hygienic in their nature.

(1) An historian is investigating the effects and treatment of shrapnel wounds and has a number of questions:

> **?** What was the nature of the wounds?

> **?** How were infections treated?

> **?** How quickly were the wounds treated?

> **?** In what conditions were soldiers treated?

> **?** What were the chances of a wound becoming infected?

> **?** How many people died from shrapnel wounds?

Annotate Source A deciding whether it could be used to answer the questions. Circle (A) and label (✏) the text.

(2) Look at Source B. Annotate the image in the source deciding whether it could be used to answer the historian's questions from **(1)**. Label (✏) the image with your thoughts.

Source B *Soldiers convalescing during the First World War. Taken by the war photographer John MacLellan between 1917 and 1918.*

2 How do I identify the limitations of a source?

When identifying how useful a source is, you must always remember to consider the possible limitations in content and its reliability. Remember, as well as how much relevant information it contains, you will need to think about:

- who created the source and their reasons for creating it – this is the source's **provenance** and it can tell you about how reliable the source is
- how typical you think the information given in the source is.

To find what the limitations of a source are and how useful it is, you need to study the provenance of the source – the **N**ature, **O**rigin and **P**urpose (NOP).

Nature	Origin	Purpose
What kind of source is it? A photo, a diary, an official record? This is the **nature** of the source.	**Who** created it and **when**? Did they witness the events first-hand? Are they having to remember events? This is the **origin** of the source.	**Why** was the source created? For a photograph: is it natural or posed? Why did the photographer pick those people or that shot? For a written account: why was it written? To entertain, to persuade someone, to reassure someone? Who was meant to read it? This is the **purpose** of the source.

1 **a** Add notes on the provenance of Source A and Source B from page 25 in the table below. The answer to some questions might be that you don't know.

	Source A	Source B
Who created the source?		
Are they an expert?		
Do they have personal interests?		
When did they create the source?		
Did they witness the events first hand?		
Why did the author/ photographer create this?		

b Which of the sources do you think is the more reliable source of information for answering an inquiry into the effects and treatment of shrapnel wounds?

....

2 Does the information in Source A agree with what you already know about the treatment of shrapnel wounds, or is it surprising? Explain your answer.

....

....

....

3 How do I include judgements about the provenance of the source?

Once you have identified what aspects of the source are useful and its limitations, you need to think about the aspects of the provenance (its nature, origin or purpose) and how they might affect how you might use the source. Thinking a source is unreliable does not mean it is useless to an historian. You need to make a judgement on how useful it is.

(1) Consider Sources A and B from page 25 comparatively by completing ✎ the table below.

	Source A	Source B
Do the nature, origin and purpose of the source provenance add strength to the usefulness of the source content?		
Do the nature, origin and purpose of the source provenance weaken the usefulness of the source content?		

(2) Choose one of the sources. Complete ✎ the following sentences to come up with a judgement on how useful the source would be to an enquiry about shrapnel wounds.

ⓐ An historian should treat Source .... with caution because

....

....

....

....

....

> Give an example of something about the provenance you feel makes the source less reliable.

> Try to explain how this might affect how you would use it.

ⓑ The provenance of this source makes it useful because ....

....

....

....

....

> Give an example of something about the provenance you feel makes the source more reliable.

> Try to explain how this might affect how you would use it.

Sample response

Read through the student's response to this exam-style question. Sources A and B are on page 25.

Exam-style question

How useful are Sources A and B for an enquiry into the treatments for shrapnel wounds?

Explain your answer, using Sources A and B and your knowledge of the historical context.

Source A is useful to an enquiry into shrapnel wounds because it implies that wounds were not being treated quickly enough. It also implies that there is a great need for well-equipped operating theatres, which suggests that surgery was used to treat wounds. Surgery had advanced a lot during the 19th century and operations were now done under anaesthetics in operating theatres that were as clean as possible using antiseptic soap and sterilisation. This source also says that there needs to be more sanitary and hygienic hospitals near the front line in France. This is to be able to operate before wounds become infected.

Source B is a photograph of wounded soldiers so it is useful in showing us the possible consequences of wounds and gives an accurate and reliable example of amputations.

Neither source gives details about the immediate effects of shrapnel wounds, nor provides any evidence on treatments other than amputation, for example Thomas splints.

A politician gave the speech in Source A in 1915; he had no first-hand experience and was relying on what other people told him. He might also be emphasising the negative aspects of wound treatment, to persuade the government to increase spending in this area.

Side annotations:
- Identifies content that is useful from Source A ☐
- Identifies content that is useful from Source B ☐
- Identifies an element of provenance that may be useful ☐
- Identifies an element of provenance that may limit how the source is used ☐

---

① Read the key features of an effective answer next to the student answer. Tick ✓ the ones you feel the student has achieved.

② Draw ✐ arrows from each ticked box and circle Ⓐ the relevant passages in the answer to show that key feature.

③ What would you add to the student's answer in order to achieve all five key features? ✐

....

....

④ Now write ✐ a conclusion to this answer on separate paper, including any judgements about how useful the sources are.

Your turn!

Now try this exam-style question using the prompts below in the student plan. Write ✏ your answer on separate paper.

Exam-style question

How useful are Sources C and D for an enquiry into the effects of gas attacks during the First World War?

Explain your answer, using Sources C and D and your knowledge of the historical context.

Source C *From the notebook of Lance Sergeant Elmer Cotton, who served in the 5th Northumberland Fusiliers in 1915. He is describing the effects of a chlorine gas attack.*

It produces a flooding of the lungs. It is the equivalent to drowning, only on dry land. The effects are these – a splitting headache and a terrific thirst (but to drink water is instant death), a knife-edge pain in the lungs and the coughing up of a greenish froth off the stomach and the lungs, finally resulting in death. It is a fiendish death to die.

Source D *From a 1919 painting by John Singer Sargent. Sargent was commissioned by the British War Memorials Committee to paint this in 1918 and researched the painting by visiting both Arras and Ypres before the end of the war. These soldiers have experienced a mustard gas attack.*

	Source C	Source D
Content strengths *What I have found out about gas attacks from the sources*		
Knowledge check *Does my own knowledge suggest this is accurate?*		
Provenance	Nature: Origin: Purpose:	Nature: Origin: Purpose:
Most useful element of provenance		
Biggest limitation of provenance		

Review your skills

Check up

Review your response to the exam-style question on page 29. Tick ✓ the column to show how well you think you have done each of the following.

	Had a go ✓	Nearly there ✓	Got it! ✓
identified the aspects of content that are useful to an historian studying the effects of shrapnel wounds (utility)	☐	☐	☐
identified elements of the provenance of the source (nature, origin, purpose) which make the source more useful (utility)	☐	☐	☐
identified accuracy of the provenance of the source (nature, origin, purpose) which means the source must be used with caution (limitations)	☐	☐	☐

Need more practice?

If you want to practise another 8-mark question, try this one.

Exam-style question

Study Sources A and B on page 25.

How useful are Sources A and B for an enquiry into the problems involved in performing operations on the Western Front?

Explain your answer, using Sources A and B and your knowledge of the historical context.   (8 marks)

How confident do you feel about each of these **skills**? Colour ✏ in the bars.

1 How do I identify what is useful to an historian?

2 How do I identify the limitations of a source?

3 How do I include judgements about the provenance of the source?

④ Answering relevantly

This unit will help you to learn how you can answer a question as relevantly as possible. The skills you will build are to:

- recognise the demands of the question
- stick to the focus of the question
- plan a relevant answer to the question.

In the exam, you will be asked to tackle a question such as the one below. This unit will prepare you to write your own response to this exam-style question.

Exam-style question

Explain **one** way in which people's beliefs about the causes of disease were the same in the seventeenth century and the fourteenth century.

(4 marks)

The three key questions in the **skills boosts** will help you to recognise the demands of the question and ensure that you answer relevantly.

 How do I read the question?

 How do I identify relevant detail?

 How do I plan my answer to ensure it answers the question?

Turn over to see one student's response to a similar exam-style question.

Look at this exam-style question:

Explain **one** way in which people's beliefs about the causes of disease were the same in the nineteenth century as they were during the seventeenth century.   **(4 marks)**

1 Highlight 🖊 what you think are the most important parts of this exam-style question.

Read this extract from a student answer for this exam-style question.

> During the nineteenth century people continued to
> believe strongly in miasmatic theory – that disease was
> caused by 'bad air'. This is a continuation in beliefs
> from the seventeenth century, when microscopes made
> it possible to study what scientists called animalcules
> in the air. This fitted in with the earlier belief that
> disease was caused by inhaling smelly, contaminated
> air. These animalcules were really bacteria, but the
> link between them and disease was not proven until
> Pasteur's germ theory in 1861 and Robert Koch's later
> work on bacteria.

2 Circle Ⓐ the sections of the answer that are about aspects staying the same.

3 Underline Ⓐ the sections of the answer that are about change.

4 Look at your selections. Highlight 🖊 those that you think are most relevant to the question.

Causes of disease

This unit uses the theme of causes of disease to build your skills in answering relevantly. If you need to review your knowledge of this theme, work through these pages.

1 Underline Ⓐ the most appropriate word from each selection to complete the description below, about the beliefs surrounding the causes of disease during the Medical Renaissance (1500–1700).

> It takes a long time for the attitudes of a society to change, and so people during the Renaissance often believed the same things caused disease as their ancestors had during the **Stone Age/Roman occupation/Middle Ages**. This meant that beliefs were predominantly **rational/supernatural**. For example, people continued to believe that God sent disease as a punishment for sins.
>
> The Renaissance was a period of change, though, and across Europe the power of the Church was in decline and people were increasingly looking to science to explain the world around them. Individuals like Vesalius and Harvey were beginning to apply this **scientific/religious/hi-tech** approach to medicine, and this would eventually lead to more **rational/supernatural** explanations for the cause of disease. However, without proof people continued to rely on ideas they knew and trusted.

2 Draw ✏ lines linking the headings on the left to the descriptions of the traditional beliefs and practices on the right.

A Anatomy	**a** The books of Galen and Hippocrates were used less and people began to observe for themselves rather than looking for what books told them.
B Astrology	**b** Belief that the body was made up of four liquids, to be kept in balance. People questioned whether external factors had a bigger influence.
C Diagnosis using urine	**c** Increased acceptance of dissection and scientific interest led to a better understanding of the human body. Vesalius and Harvey practised it.
D Influence of the Church	**d** Another explanation for disease that became less popular. While scientists continued to explore the skies, its role in medicine diminished.
E Miasma	**e** Increasingly abandoned as a tool, as people questioned the role of eating the wrong things. Doctors decided it was not directly related to health.
F Theory of the Four Humours	**f** The idea that inhaling bad smells/air causes illness continued, as interest in external factors grew and following an increase in epidemics.
G Use of medical books	**g** As scientific enquiry increased, people questioned whether God sent disease. Humanists criticised people's reliance on the Church for explanations, encouraging them to instead observe the human body.

③ In the table below there are some **new ideas** of the 17th century hidden among the traditional beliefs about the causes of disease.

a Highlight 🖉 the **rational** beliefs and highlight in another colour the **supernatural** beliefs about the causes of disease. This will help you to see whether new ideas were predominantly rational or supernatural. Fill in 🖉 the key to help you.

Rational [   ]   Supernatural [   ]

Four Humours	Miasma	Punishment from God
Blood not used up and replaced (Harvey)	Clinical observations key to understanding disease (Sydenham)	Animalcules (Royal Society publication)
Dissections to better understand the body	Evil spirits	Astrology (impact of the position of stars and planets)

b Now circle Ⓐ the ideas that are new to the 17th century.

④ Using the information in the table above, list 🖉 the new ideas that you have circled under the correct factor of influence.

Factor of influence	New ideas
Scientific discovery	
Understanding of anatomy	
Questioning of the Church	
Suggestions by key individuals, e.g. Thomas Sydenham	
New technology such as Leeuwenhoek's microscope	

⑤ Fill in 🖉 the blanks using the words in the word box.

New religious ideas questioned the power of the .... This made it more difficult for the Church to put forward its ideas about .... Although people were still ...., they were more prepared to look for different explanations for why .... occurred. People began to believe that disease was not caused by ....

God	religious	diseases
science	Catholic Church	

How do I read the question?

To identify the focus so you can answer the exam question relevantly you need to:
- look at the time period(s) mentioned – the **time parameter**
- identify the **topic/theme** the question is asking you to focus on
- make **comparisons** to determine how much things changed or stayed the same.

The exam question will cover **time parameters** or time periods.

(1) The time periods you may be asked about will often be centuries. Label ⊘ the timeline with the correct century name. One has been done for you.

1200.................................1300.........................1400. *15th century* .1500............................1600.............................

1700.................................1800.........................1900............................2000............................

(2) Look at the exam-style question below and circle Ⓐ the **time parameters**.

Exam-style question

Explain **one** way in which people's reactions to the plague in Britain were similar in the fourteenth and seventeenth centuries.   **(4 marks)**

The question will also ask you to focus on one of the **topics/common themes** you have studied in the Medicine thematic study, such as:

? what people believed caused disease

? who cared for the sick and where

? how illness was treated or prevented

? which factors influenced medicine, e.g. key individuals, science and technology, religion.

(3) Look at the exam-style question below and underline Ⓐ the **topic/theme**.

Exam-style question

Explain **one** way in which people's beliefs about the causes of disease were different in the nineteenth century to the sixteenth century.   **(4 marks)**

Finally, you need to identify what **comparisons** the question is asking you to make, whether things are similar or different between the two time periods and how. Answering how things were the same/different is key to explaining.

(4) Look at the exam-style question below and highlight ⊘ the **comparison focus**.

Exam-style question

Explain **one** way in which people's beliefs about the causes of disease were different in the nineteenth century and the seventeenth century.   **(4 marks)**

To be relevant your answer must stick to the time period(s), topic and comparison focus identified in the question. Anything outside of this could be considered irrelevant.

(5) Look again at the three exam-style questions on this page and, where you haven't already, circle Ⓐ the time parameter, underline Ⓐ the topic/theme and highlight ⊘ the comparison focus for each one.

2 How do I identify relevant detail?

To develop your answer it is necessary to support the focus you have identified in the question with relevant details from your own knowledge.

(1) Look at the exam-style question below. Circle Ⓐ the time parameters, underline Ⓐ the topic/theme focus and highlight 🖉 the comparison focus.

Exam-style question

Explain **one** way in which people's beliefs about the causes of disease were the same in the seventeenth century as they were in the thirteenth century.

(4 marks)

(2) A student has made the following notes from their own knowledge to answer the above question. Circle Ⓐ which of the detailed knowledge sections below is relevant to answering this question.

A During the seventeenth century people continued to believe in old ideas such as the belief that illness was caused by bad smells or bad air that was inhaled. Scientists studied the air under microscopes and found animalcules, which they believed were proof of bad air.

B In the mid-nineteenth century a scientist called Louis Pasteur discovered that animalcules were germinating inside liquids and called them germs. Robert Koch later made the link between 'germs' and disease.

C During the seventeenth century William Harvey started to question the use of books by Hippocrates and Galen to understand the human body, and started to investigate for themselves. This led to a more accurate knowledge of human anatomy.

People's beliefs

D While some individuals started to question the power of God to send disease, many people still turned to the Church for guidance and explanation during times of desperation, for example during outbreaks of the plague or other epidemics.

E Despite the work of some key individuals, there were few new ideas that weren't simply theories. So day-to-day physicians still used old medical books and ideas such as the Four Humours. Doctors commonly diagnosed 'too much blood'.

F During the sixteenth century doctors and apothecaries started to use scientific approaches, such as alchemy, to treat and even try and cure illness.

(3) The detailed knowledge above is historically accurate, but:

> For these 4-mark questions, you only need to talk about **one** way in which things changed or stayed the same.

a explain 🖉 why note B is not relevant to answering the question

....

....

b explain 🖉 why note C is not relevant to the question

....

....

c explain 🖉 why note F is not relevant to the question.

....

....

How do I plan my answer to ensure it answers the question?

As well as selecting relevant content knowledge to support your answer, it is important that you explain how there was a similarity or a difference.

Look at the following exam-style question and the example student answer below it.

Exam-style question

Explain **one** way in which treatments for illness in the nineteenth century were different from treatments for illness in the present day. **(4 marks)**

One way in which treatments for disease are different today from the nineteenth century is that we can now cure infections using antibiotics. In the nineteenth century people often died from infected wounds because there was no effective treatment. Today antibiotics, for example penicillin, are used to fight infection.

One way to make sure your answer answers the question is to use the following checklist.

Checklist Have I:	✓
identified one difference?	
selected content knowledge for that difference for the first time period required?	
selected content knowledge for that difference for the second time period required?	
explained how there is a similarity or a difference?	

(1) Tick ✓ the checklist to decide if everything necessary has been covered in the sample student answer.

You can use specific language to make it clear that you have identified whether there is a similarity or a difference. Here are some words and phrases that will help you to do this.

still	remained	continued	however
persisted	also	changed	but
was now	in contrast	are different	whereas

(2) Read through the sample student answer above and highlight ✐ where they have used words to show similarity or difference.

(3) Have a go at rewriting ✐ the answer above to include more of the phrases from the word box.

....

....

....

....

....

....

Sample response

Read through the student's response to the following exam-style question.

Exam-style question

Explain **one** way in which people's beliefs about the causes of disease were the same in the seventeenth century as they were in the fourteenth century.

(4 marks)

During the fourteenth century it was a common belief that God sent disease as a punishment for people's sins. In the seventeenth century people still believed in God, but also people had started to question the idea that God was in control of every aspect of life and in particular fewer people believed that God sent disease. During the seventeenth century scientific discoveries were being made and people became more concerned with external factors causing disease. The medieval idea of miasma and bad smells still fitted with these ideas, so people and doctors continued to use them as an explanation for disease during the seventeenth century. This idea was developed when animalcules were discovered but the principle was the same – disease was caused by contaminated air.

① Complete ✐ the details below to decide upon the focus of the exam-style question.

Time period: ....

Topic/theme: ....

Comparison: ....

② Highlight ✐ the sections of the student's answer you think are most relevant to the focus of this question.

③ **a** Cross out (~~cat~~) any sections that are not relevant to the question and therefore unnecessary for the student to include in their answer.

   b Why are these sections irrelevant? (Think about the focus you identified.) ✐

   ....

   ....

④ What advice would you give this student to help them to improve their answer? ✐

| Consider how you might instruct them on: |
| • what to take note of when reading the question |
| • how to avoid including irrelevant information. |

   ....

   ....

   ....

   ....

   ....

   ....

   ....

Your turn!

Now try this exam-style question using the prompts below.

Exam-style question

Explain **one** way in which people's beliefs about the causes of disease were different in the seventeenth century and fourteenth century.

(4 marks)

(**1**) In the exam-style question,

   (**a**) circle (A) the time parameters

   (**b**) underline (A) the topic/theme focus.

(**2**) List (✎) four pieces of content knowledge relevant to the question. Include as much detail as possible.

....

....

(**3**) Look at your notes above and highlight (✎) the content knowledge that most clearly shows one difference between the time periods.

(**4**) Write (✎) a brief bullet point plan of your answer.

(**5**) Now write (✎) your response to the question on a separate piece of paper. As you write, think carefully about:

- the relevance of the details you are using
- explaining the comparison between the two periods clearly.

Review your skills

Check up

Review your response to the exam-style question on page 39. Tick ⊘ the column to show how well you think you have done each of the following.

	Had a go ✓	Nearly there ✓	Got it! ✓
identified the time parameters of the question	☐	☐	☐
identified the topic or theme focus	☐	☐	☐
selected content knowledge that was relevant to the question	☐	☐	☐
compared the situation between the two periods clearly	☐	☐	☐

Need more practice?

You will need to practise what has been covered in this unit to answer other exam-style questions in this workbook. If you want to practise another 4 mark similarity and difference question, try ⊘ this one:

Exam-style question

Explain **one** way in which understanding of the causes of disease and illness was different in the eighteenth century from the present day.

(4 marks)

How confident do you feel about each of these **skills**? Colour ⊘ in the bars.

1 How do I read the question?

2 How do I identify relevant detail?

3 How do I plan my answer to ensure it answers the question?

⑤ Selecting and using supporting evidence

This unit will help you to select and deploy relevant supporting evidence from your content knowledge in your answers.

The skills you will build are to:

- select information relevant to the question
- ensure that the evidence selected is the most relevant to the concept (i.e. change or causes)
- move beyond the suggested content and include relevant ideas of your own.

In the exam, you will be asked to tackle a question such as the one below. This unit will prepare you to write your own response to this exam-style question.

Exam-style question

Explain why there was very little change in how illness was prevented and treated during the period c1250–c1500.

You may use the following in your answer:

- the theory of the Four Humours
- punishments for sin.

You **must** also use information of your own.   (12 marks)

The three key questions in the **skills boosts** will help you to select and deploy supporting evidence.

 1 How do I select information to answer the question?

 2 How do I ensure that information is relevant to the concept focus?

 3 How do I use information of my own?

Look at the following exam-style question and the student plan beneath it.

Exam-style question

Explain why there was little change in ideas about the causes of disease during the period c1250–c1500.

You may use the following in your answer:

- the Church
- Galen.

You **must** also use information of your own.

(12 marks)

Paragraph 1: The Church

- Because people didn't have scientific explanations for the causes of disease, they still believed that it was a punishment sent by God for their sins. People continued to follow the advice of the Church regarding illness and often used prayer and repentance as a way of preventing disease.

- The theory of the Four Humours fitted well with the Church, so the Church supported it and monks copied these books so they could be used to teach physicians.

Paragraph 2: Galen and the Four Humours

- The Church banned dissection, so doctors and surgeons were reliant on the anatomical teachings of Galen, despite the fact he dissected animals and some of his teachings were later proven to be wrong.

- Doctors continued to use Galen's Theory of Opposites to restore the balance of the humours in their patients. Bloodletting and purges remained common treatments for illness.

(1) In the table below, note ✎ which of the ideas in the plan are relevant to the question.

Think about:

- the focus of the question – little change in ideas about the cause of disease
- the time period (1250–1500)
- the concept – causation. Why was there little change?

(2) Note ✎ down three other pieces of supporting evidence the student could consider.

Relevant ideas	Other supporting evidence

Medieval ideas on the causes of disease

This unit uses the theme of medieval ideas on the causes of disease to build your skills in selecting and using supporting evidence. If you need to review your knowledge of this theme, work through these pages.

(1) Look at the medieval explanations for disease below.

- Highlight (✏) the **supernatural** beliefs about the causes of disease.
- Circle (Ⓐ) the **rational** explanations.

> **Supernatural explanations**: Ideas about causes that rely on faith, as there is no evidence of their power or existence.
> **Rational explanations**: Based on observations and causes from nature.

Galen wrote the Theory of the Four Humours and the Theory of Opposites to treat imbalance.	People didn't want to risk going to Hell, so they listened to what the Church told them. They made an effort to live a sin-free life, prayed and acted upon any penances (punishments) the priests gave them. Flagellation (whipping yourself) was a common self-punishment.	The Theory of the Four Humours stated that illness occurred when the body's four liquids (humours) were out of balance. Ancient doctors had observed that the world was made up of four elements and four seasons, so it followed that the body had four humours and this linked to disease.
Malnutrition – people believed that God punished people by sending famines. People who survived them believed God had forgiven them through prayer.	People believed that lepers (people with the skin disease leprosy) had sinned and the disease was a sign of their sin. There was no cure and lepers were usually banished from the community.	Miasma was the belief that evil fumes could contaminate the air. Bad smells were believed to be an indication of air that contained disease.
The balance of the body could be controlled through diet, bloodletting and purging (vomiting).	Astrology – the movement of the stars and planets affects diseases and their symptoms.	In the later Middle Ages, doctors were trained at universities to use clinical observations and the Four Humours, following the teachings of Hippocrates and Galen.

(2) **a** Circle (Ⓐ) the statement below that you think best describes beliefs about the causes of disease during the Middle Ages.

Predominantly rational	Predominantly supernatural	An even mix of explanations

b Explain (✏) why you made this decision. Consider the significance of the ideas, not just the number of them.

....

....

③ Twelve different medieval treatments for disease are described below. Classify each of the treatments by colouring ✏ in the box beside each heading, to show which of the following remedy categories it fits. To help you, add ✏ your colour code to the key below.

Superstitions and faith ☐   Four Humours ☐

Herbal ☐

④ Under each description, explain ✏ why someone in the Middle Ages might use this treatment. Try to relate your answer to the believed causes of disease (rational or supernatural).

☐ Pilgrimage	☐ Fasting	☐ Prayer/Mass
A journey to an important religious monument, shrine or place.	Going without food.	Healing prayers and incantations (spells).
☐ The king's touch	☐ Nothing	☐ Astrology
It was widely believed that the king had the power to heal certain illnesses because of his 'divine right'. This was considered particularly effective for scrofula.	Occasionally people were discouraged from seeking cures. If God had sent the disease to purge the soul, it was important for the disease to run its course.	The position of the stars and planets was used to write a horoscope, which was used to diagnose and suggest treatments.
☐ Bloodletting	☐ Purging	☐ Clyster
Phlebotomy or bloodletting involved removing excess blood from the body through a cut or by using leeches.	Clearing the digestive system of 'bad food', either by taking a laxative to cause bowel movements or taking a purgative to make you vomit.	Like an enema – used to wash out your bowels.
☐ Drinks	☐ Food	☐ Bathing
People would drink herbal infusions. Often the recommended ingredients were very expensive.	Commonly included spicy, warming foods such as ginger, pepper and cardamom.	Hot baths to steam out impurities and administer herbal remedies. Regimen Sanitatis was a set of ideas about hygiene.

How do I select information to answer the question?

In these questions you must use your own content knowledge, but selection must be relevant to the question.

Look again at this exam-style question:

Exam-style question

Explain why there was little change in ideas about the causes of disease during the period c1250–c1500.

You may use the following in your answer:

- the Church
- Galen.

You **must** also use information of your own.

(12 marks)

1 **a** Circle Ⓐ the focus topic/theme.

   b Highlight ✏️ the time period.

   c Underline A̲ the concept. What is the question asking you to do?

> These indicators will help you to select relevant evidence from your own knowledge.

2 Look at the spider diagram of content knowledge below.

   a Cross out ⊝ any content knowledge that does not fit the topic/theme focus.

   b Cross out ⊝ any content knowledge that does not fit the time parameters.

   c Cross out ⊝ any content knowledge that does not fit the concept.

   d Write ✏️ what content knowledge you are left with.

....

....

> Everything you are left with should be relevant to the question, and can be used as supporting evidence in your answer.

- Punishment for sins
- Malnutrition
- Herbal remedies through drinks and baths
- Content knowledge
- Scientists had identified animalcules in the air
- The Theory of the Four Humours

2 How do I ensure that information is relevant to the concept focus?

Each 'Explain why…' question will ask you to explain why something either changed or stayed the same. It is important to identify which it is asking for and explain how your supporting evidence explains this. The exam-style question on page 45, is asking you to explain why there was **little change**.

① a The exam-style question on page 45 suggests you may use 'Galen' and 'the Church' in your answer. Read the student answer below and underline Ⓐ the reason(s) they give for Galen leading to a period of little change in beliefs about the causes of disease during the Middle Ages.

> There was little change in ideas about the causes of disease during the Middle Ages because physicians continued to read the works of ancient doctors such as Galen. Galen was a doctor in Ancient Rome who wrote about the Theory of the Four Humours. This was a rational theory about the cause of disease first developed by the Ancient Greeks. It was based on the belief that disease was caused by an imbalance of bodily fluids or 'humours'. It was linked to the world being created in fours – four seasons, four elements etc… As the Church supported the logic behind the theory, physicians were trained by reading Galen's work and they continued to use the Theory of the Four Humours to explain disease.

b Circle Ⓐ which of the following best summarise(s) the reason(s) you have identified.

Doctors were trained using Galen's books.	There were no alternative ideas about what was causing disease.	The rational ideas were accepted by the Church.

② Note ✐ down one piece of content knowledge other than the Four Humours that would help you to explain why there was **little change**.

....

③ Explain ✐ why this piece of content knowledge led to a period of little change.

....

....

....

3   How do I use information of my own?

To move beyond the ideas given in the question you will need to write a third paragraph that, while still relevant to the topic focus, time parameters and concept, is not related to the two bullet-pointed prompts.

The bullet-pointed prompts in the exam-style question on page 45 are 'the Church' and 'Galen'.

The table below includes ideas to answer this question. All are relevant to beliefs about the causes of disease during the Middle Ages.

Astrology	People didn't want to risk going to Hell, so they listened to what the Church told them.	The Four Humours
People believed that lepers had sinned and their skin disease was a sign of their sin.	Malnutrition	Miasma
Galen wrote about the Theory of the Four Humours.		In the later Middle Ages, universities trained doctors to use clinical observations and the Four Humours, following the teachings of Hippocrates and Galen.

①   Cross out (~~cat~~) any ideas that are related to 'the Church' or 'Galen'.

②   Select one of the ideas you have left and use this to plan 🖉 a third paragraph in the table below.

Third point	
Supporting detail (from own knowledge)	
Explain why it led to little change	

Sample response

Read through the student's response to this exam-style question.

Exam-style question

Explain why there was little change in ideas about the causes of disease during the period c1250–c1500.

You may use the following in your answer:

- the Church

- Galen.

You **must** also use information of your own. (12 marks)

The Church was very influential in there being little change in ideas about the causes of disease during the Middle Ages. Because people didn't have scientific explanations for the causes of disease they still believed that disease was a punishment for their sins sent by God. People continued to follow the advice of the Church regarding illness and often used prayer and repentance as disease prevention. The Theory of the Four Humours fitted well with the Church, so the Church supported it and monks copied these books so they could be used to teach physicians.

The Church also banned dissection, so doctors and surgeons were reliant on the anatomical teachings of Galen, despite the fact he dissected animals and some of his teachings were later proven to be wrong. Doctors continued to use Galen's Theory of Opposites to restore the balance of the humours in their patients, and bloodletting and purges remained common treatments for illness.

Finally, people continued to believe that the air had something to do with the spread of disease. Romans had avoided building their homes near swamps and other features that emitted bad smells, due to the belief that these bad smells were an indication of and commonly present with disease. As the cause of disease could not be seen, people in the Middle Ages continued to believe it might be in the air. For this reason the rational explanation of miasma – bad air – continued to be used.

(1) In the student response above:

a Highlight ✎ evidence that is relevant to the topic/theme focus of '**little change in ideas about the causes of disease**'.

b Underline Ⓐ evidence that is **not** relevant to the time period **c1250–c1500**.

c Circle Ⓐ evidence that is an attempt to explain how this **caused** little change in ideas about the causes of disease.

d Highlight in another colour ✎ evidence that is not based on either of the bullet-pointed ideas from the exam-style question.

Your turn!

Now try this exam-style question using the prompts below.

Explain why there was very little change in how illness was prevented and treated during the period c1250–c1500.

You may use the following in your answer:

- the Theory of the Four Humours
- punishments for sin.

You **must** also use information of your own.

(12 marks)

(1) First, identify the indicators in the exam-style question that will ensure your selection of supporting evidence is relevant. ✎

Topic/theme focus: ....

Time parameters: ....

Concept: ....

(2) On a separate piece of paper, create ✎ a spider diagram of relevant knowledge. Remember to include the two bullet-pointed ideas from the exam-style question as well as at least one other.

(3) Plan ✎ your answer using the template below.

Relevant idea 1: ....

Supporting evidence – details from content knowledge:

....

....

Explanation of how this detail led to change/little change – answers the question:

....

....

....

Relevant idea 2: ....

Supporting evidence – details from content knowledge:

....

....

Explanation of how this detail led to change/little change – answers the question:

....

....

....

Relevant idea 3: ....

Supporting evidence – details from content knowledge:

....

....

Explanation of how this detail led to change/little change – answers the question:

....

....

....

Review your skills

Check up

Review your response to the exam-style question on page 49. Tick ✓ the column to show how well you think you have done each of the following.

	Had a go ✓	Nearly there ✓	Got it! ✓
used supporting evidence relevant to the topic/theme	☐	☐	☐
used supporting evidence relevant to the time period	☐	☐	☐
used supporting detail relevant to the concept	☐	☐	☐
used supporting evidence that goes beyond the two prompts provided	☐	☐	☐

Need more practice?

You will need to practise what has been covered in this unit to answer other exam-style questions in this workbook. If you want to practise another 12-mark question, try 🖉 this one:

Exam-style question

Explain why there was rapid change in the prevention of disease in the period c1750–c1900.

You may use the following in your answer:

- inoculation
- Edward Jenner.

You **must** also use information of your own.

(12 marks)

How confident do you feel about each of these **skills**? Colour 🖉 in the bars.

1 How do I select information to answer the question?

2 How do I ensure that information is relevant to the concept focus?

3 How do I use information of my own?

⑥ Understanding change

This unit will help you to understand how historians identify and study change. Change is happening all the time. The skills you will build are to:

- identify changes that are historically significant
- describe this significance in your answers.

In the exam, you will be asked to tackle questions such as the one below. This unit will prepare you to write your own response to the following exam-style question. These questions are worth 16 marks – plus 4 marks for SPaG and specialist terminology.

Exam-style question

'Ideas about the causes of disease changed significantly in the period c1700–c1900'.

How far do you agree? Explain your answer.

You may use the following in your answer:

- spontaneous generation
- Louis Pasteur.

You **must** also use information of your own.

(16 marks) + (4 marks)

The three key questions in the **skills boosts** will help you to identify and describe historically significant change in a period.

① How do I know what makes a change historically significant?

② How do I distinguish between change and continuity?

③ How do I decide how significant a change is?

Look at the student's plan below for an answer to the exam-style question on page 51. Notice that they plan to give:

- two arguments to support the statement
- one argument against the statement.

They have also included the two suggested ideas from the exam-style question and one of their own.

Paragraph 1:

<u>Point</u>: Significant change in ideas → Louis Pasteur and Robert Koch proved link between human disease and bacteria (microorganisms).

<u>Evidence (supporting own knowledge)</u>: Progress already started in this period. Theory of Four Humours abandoned. Spontaneous generation instead because of more study of microbes. Still wrong but basis of Pasteur's work. Pasteur – microbes in decaying matter caused decay not a product of it.

Paragraph 2:

<u>Point</u>: Ideas about causes of disease did change but not significantly and they weren't totally accepted by everyone immediately. Pasteur only published his criticisms of 'spontaneous generation' in 1861. 'Germ theory' not immediately accepted as the cause of disease.

<u>Evidence (supporting own knowledge)</u>: Pasteur unable to prove link between germs and human disease because had to kill the 'germs' by heating. Koch: later in the century stained and identified specific bacteria that caused disease in humans → vaccines for human diseases. Only then was 'germ theory' accepted.

Paragraph 3:

<u>Point</u>: Change from causes of disease being a battle – supernatural vs rational explanations.

<u>Evidence (supporting own knowledge)</u>: People still religious → some criticism of new treatments (such as anaesthetics) seen as against God's will. Scientific, rational explanation did become only explanation for disease. Tie between religion and the cause of disease cut.

---

(1) Read the student's plan above and:

   (a) Highlight 🖉 the two paragraphs that identify significant change (agreeing with the statement).

   (b) Circle Ⓐ the paragraph that identifies a limitation in how significant change was during this period (disagreeing with the statement).

(2) Read the student's notes for paragraph 3, which are based on evidence from the student's own knowledge.

   (a) From your own knowledge, what other example could you use to argue that change in ideas about the causes of disease was or was not significant during the period c1700–c1900? Write 🖉 your answer below.

....

....

....

   (b) Give one reason why you chose that example. 🖉

....

....

....

....

....

Changes in medicine, c1700–c1900

This unit uses the theme of changes in medicine, c1700–c1900, to build your skills in understanding change. If you need to review your knowledge of this theme, work through these pages.

1. Read the four pieces of information related to changes in medicine that took place throughout the period, in the flow diagram below. In the empty boxes, write ✐ an explanation of why these led to new ideas.

The Church was becoming less important in people's lives.	The growth in cities meant an increased risk of disease, so understanding the causes of disease became a priority.	Theories such of the Theory of the Four Humours were abandoned as it became increasingly apparent that treatments based on these theories didn't work.	Microscopes enabled microbes – 'animalcules' – to be studied further.

New ideas such as 'spontaneous generation' developed.

2. Look at the statements below.

   a. In one colour, highlight ✐ the statements that accurately describe **spontaneous generation** (the original idea about microbes).

   b. In a different colour, highlight ✐ the statements that accurately describe **germ theory** (by which Pasteur successfully made the link between 'germs' and disease).

Early alternative to the Four Humours	Microbes **cause** matter to decay	Decaying matter **produces** microbes rather than them **causing** decay	Microbes are produced once an animal or plant dies or starts rotting	Microbes cause death or the rotting process by increasing in number (germinating)	Microbes cannot survive in sterile conditions and can be killed using heat

To help you, colour these boxes to show which highlight colour shows which.

Spontaneous generation ☐   Germ theory ☐

3. Louis Pasteur was unable to prove the link between microbes and human disease. However, Pasteur's germ theory inspired the work and investigations of Robert Koch.

What technique did Koch develop to decisively prove the link between human diseases and germs? ✐

....

....

....

④ Read statements A–K below, which tell the story of the development of germ theory and the understanding of the role of bacteria in the cause of disease. Number 🖉 the statements to show the correct chronological order.

A John Snow closed the Broad Street pump to demonstrate that cholera was caused by contaminated water. ☐	G Robert Koch's work and methodology enabled other doctors to discover different types of bacteria. ☐
B Joseph Lister encouraged the use of carbolic soap and spray in hospitals. ☐	H Robert Koch discovered the microbe that caused tuberculosis. ☐
C Louis Pasteur discovered that microbes caused wine to decay. ☐	I John Tyndall gave a lecture linking his work on dust particles with Pasteur's germ theory. ☐
D Robert Koch developed a dye to stain different bacteria, in order to observe and identify them. ☐	J Ideas about miasma dominated. ☐
E People explained decay through a belief in 'spontaneous generation'. ☐	K Louis Pasteur published his germ theory. ☐
F Leeuwenhoek observed microbes and wrote to the Royal Society about them. ☐	

⑤ Read through the preventions and treatments below. Which illustrate **change** and which illustrate **continuity** between the Renaissance (c1500–c1700) and the Industrial Age (c1750–c1900)? Colour code 🖉 the statements to show your decisions. To help you, add 🖉 your colour code to the key.

Colour key: Change ☐   Continuity ☐

Nightingale wards had hand washing, clean bedding and a controlled diet.	Carbolic soap and carbolic acid were used to clean hospital environments.	Many people were still treated at home by family members for most illnesses.	Treatments were bought from apothecaries.
Quack or 'patent remedies' remained popular.	Pasteur and Koch had discovered bacteria that caused some diseases and could create a weakened strain to be used as a vaccine.	The government started to take responsibility for sanitary conditions, introducing two public health Acts and a sewer system in London.	Edward Jenner discovered a vaccine for small pox by using cow pox, a less serious disease that created the same antibodies.
The development of anaesthetics and antiseptics improved surgical outcomes.	Blood loss was still an issue in surgical procedures.	Antiseptics were a prevention of infection but not a cure once infection during surgical treatment set in.	Some people opposed vaccination and anaesthetics on the grounds they interfered with God's will.

⑥ Read the two statements below and circle Ⓐ the option you think is a better description of treatments during the Industrial Revolution.

Treatments changed rapidly as a result of developments in our understanding of what caused disease.	Treatments changed little despite developments in our understanding of what caused disease.

1 How do I know what makes a change historically significant?

Make sure you respond appropriately to a question that asks you about the extent something changed. It is a common misconception that change is when something happens. Remember: events themselves are not change. Rather, change is when the consequences of events are historically significant.

(1) **a** Read the statements below. Some are **descriptions of events** and some are **descriptions of change**. Highlight (✏) the statements to show which are which. To help you, add (✏) your colour code to the key.

Colour key: Descriptions of events ▢   Descriptions of change ▢

In 1861 Louis Pasteur published his germ theory, criticising the theory of spontaneous generation.	In 1882, Robert Koch discovered the bacteria that caused tuberculosis.	From their reading of Pasteur's germ theory, doctors began to alter their understanding of human disease. Based on Pasteur's descriptions of reducing bacteria by heating liquids and halting the decaying process by keeping matter in a sterile environment, practices began to change.
Scientists such as Louis Pasteur were inspired to study the behaviour of microorganisms and test theories such as spontaneous generation. Through experimentation they realised the old theories were wrong and developed new explanations that stood up to testing.	In 1668 Leeuwenhoek developed the microscope which allowed study into the behaviour of microorganisms.	A study of the bacteria that caused tuberculosis along with studies of other identified bacteria led to a series of vaccines being created. This meant a number of serious diseases in humans were now preventable.

b Now complete the flow diagram below by writing (✏) a summary of the descriptions above, so that each 'event' links to the 'change' it led to.

Event   Change

2 How do I distinguish between change and continuity?

It is a common misconception that continuity is simply the absence of change – small changes are happening all the time. Continuity is when the changes in a period lack historical significance. For example, after a General Election there may be a change in the political party running the country, but if they pursue similar policies to their predecessor it may feel like a period of continuity. In the thematic study paper, the 16-mark exam question will often ask you about change and continuity between two dates, events or periods.

You can practise identifying change and continuity using timelines like the ones below.

Timeline of changes in beliefs about the causes of disease

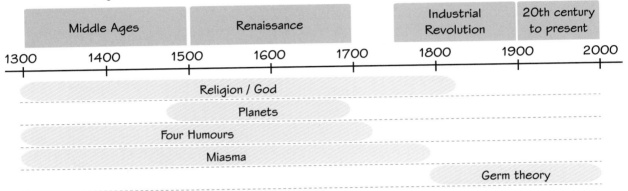

	Middle Ages		Renaissance			Industrial Revolution	20th century to present
1300	1400	1500	1600	1700	1800	1900	2000

Religion / God

Planets

Four Humours

Miasma

Germ theory

Timeline of changes in preventions and treatments for illness

	Middle Ages		Renaissance			Industrial Revolution	20th century to present
1300	1400	1500	1600	1700	1800	1900	2000

Herbal remedies

Prayer

Bloodletting and purges

Avoiding bad smells

Amputations and simple surgery – no anaesthetics and high risk of infection

Antiseptic, anaesthetised surgery

Vaccination

Antibiotics

(1) Using the information in the timelines above, write 🖊 your answers to the following questions. During which time period was there:

(a) the most change in ideas about the causes of disease? ....

(b) the most continuity in ideas about the causes of disease? ....

(c) the most change in preventing and treating illnesses? ....

(d) the most continuity in preventing and treating illnesses? ....

(2) On a separate piece of paper, write 🖊 a bullet-point plan for a question that asks whether you agree:

(a) the Renaissance was a period of change

(b) there was continuity between the Middle Ages and the end of the Renaissance.

> The timelines above may help you when writing your plans.

3 How do I decide how significant a change is?

When answering questions on change, you need to be able to identify and select those changes that are the most historically significant. You can determine the historical significance of changes by judging their impact using different criteria.

1 Read through the changes in the period c1650–c1900 listed below.

A 1861: Pasteur identified microbes in wine and was able to kill them using heat	**B** Koch developed a new method of growing and observing bacteria	**C** 1854: John Snow's maps revealed the Broad Street water pump to be a potential source of cholera	**D** 1882: Koch identified the bacteria causing tuberculosis
E Dr Bastian promoted the theory of spontaneous generation	**F** Joseph Lister made the link between germ theory and post-operative infection	**G** John Tyndall claimed that disease was spread through dust particles	**H** Leeuwenhoek used his microscope to observe and write about microbes

a Now consider the criteria for significance below. For each criterion, select an example from the above table of changes that fits it. You may find that an example fits in more than one criterion. Write the letter of your example in the table below.

Significance criteria	Example
Immediate impact: This change had a big impact at the time it happened. People noticed their lives were different as a result.	
Impact on ideas: People's ideas (e.g. beliefs about the cause of disease) were significantly different as a result.	
Widespread impact: This change affected a large number of people from different geographical areas of the world or from a range of different social groups.	
On-going impact: This one change caused a number of other changes to happen (knock-on effects).	
Long-term impact: The impact of this change continued to affect people's lives for a long time or still has an impact on how we live our lives today. It has long-term significance.	

b Consider the changes above. Were any of them **not** historically significant?

....

....

c Which change fits most of the criteria for significance? Write an explanation for your decision below using the sentence starter to help you.

This is the most significant change because ....

....

....

....

Sample response

Use what you have learned in this unit to complete the student's response to this exam-style question.

1. Read the student's response. On a separate piece of paper, write ✎ an explanation for the end of each paragraph to:

   - link the answer back to the question
   - explain **either** why this change was significant **or** why its significance was limited.

Exam-style question

'Ideas about the causes of disease changed significantly in the period c1700–c1900.'
How far do you agree? Explain your answer.

You may use the following in your answer:

- spontaneous generation
- Louis Pasteur.

You **must** also use your own information.   (16 marks) + (4 marks)

Paragraph 1:

Point: There was significant change in ideas because Louis Pasteur and Robert Koch made and proved the link between human disease and bacteria (microorganisms).

Evidence (supporting own knowledge): Progress started during this period when the Theory of the Four Humours was abandoned in favour of the idea of spontaneous generation. This change resulted from study into microbes. However, the theory was incorrect and the basis for Pasteur's work. Although Pasteur agreed that microbes were present in decaying matter he believed they caused decay rather than being a product of it.

> Why was this a significant change?

Paragraph 2:

Point: Although ideas about the cause of disease did change during the period, this change was not very significant. Pasteur did not publish his criticisms of 'spontaneous generation' until 1861 and his 'germ theory' was not immediately accepted as the cause of disease.

Evidence (supporting own knowledge): Because Pasteur's work relied on heating liquids to kill 'germs' and prevent decay, he was unable to completely prove the link to disease in humans. It was not until later in the century, as Koch started to stain and identify specific bacteria that caused disease and create vaccines for human diseases, that people started to accept the 'germ theory' as an explanation.

> Why was this a limitation to the significance of change?

Paragraph 3:

Point: Understanding about the causes of disease was no longer a battle between supernatural and rational explanations.

Evidence (supporting own knowledge): People remained religious and there was some criticism of the resulting treatments (such as anaesthetics) for meddling with God's will. However, scientific, rational explanations of disease became the only explanation for disease and the tie between religion and disease was cut.

> Why was this a significant change?

Conclusion: This was a period of significant change. Although it took most of the period c1700–c1900 for these changes to be fully accepted, there is great significance in the move away from the Theory of the Four Humours being the key rational explanation for the causes of disease.

Your turn!

Now try planning and writing your own answer to the following exam-style question.

'Approaches to the treatment and prevention of disease changed little between c1750 and c1900.' How far do you agree? Explain your answer.

You may use the following in your answer:

- bloodletting
- antibiotics.

You **must** also use information of your own.

(16 marks) + (4 marks)

Plan to write three paragraphs, developing three separate lines of argument that answer the question. (Note that paragraph 3 can be used to either agree or disagree with the statement.)

Write 🖊 a plan for your answer below before writing it out in full on a separate sheet of paper.

Paragraph 1: Treatments and prevention changed little...	Paragraph 2: Treatments and prevention changed significantly...
Point:	Point:
Evidence:	Evidence:
Explanation:	Explanation:

Paragraph 3: Separate line of argument that either agrees or disagrees with the statement	Conclusion:
Point:	
Evidence:	
Explanation:	

You could use the second timeline on page 56 to first select relevant examples of change and then give each a significance rating.

Review your skills

Check up

Review your response to the exam-style question on page 59. Tick ⊘ the column to show how well you think you have done each of the following.

	Had a go ⊘	Nearly there ⊘	Got it! ⊘
identified a significant change, relevant to the question, and explained why it was significant	☐	☐	☐
identified a continuity or limitation to the significance of the changes, relevant to the question, and explained why it was significant	☐	☐	☐
made a judgement about whether the period was one of continuity	☐	☐	☐

Need more practice?

If you want to practise another exam-style question, try ⊘ this one.

Exam-style question

'There was little change in medical treatments in Britain during the Renaissance period (c1500–c1700).'

How far do you agree? Explain your answer.

You may use the following in your answer:

• the work of William Harvey

• bloodletting and purging.

You **must** also use information of your own.

(16 marks) + (4 marks)

How confident do you feel about each of these **skills**? Colour ⊘ in the bars.

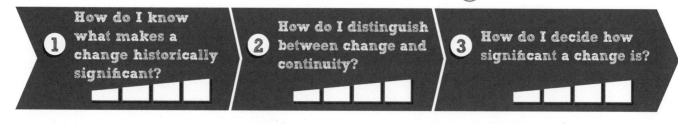

1 How do I know what makes a change historically significant?

2 How do I distinguish between change and continuity?

3 How do I decide how significant a change is?

⑦ Making links between points

This unit will help you to develop the vocabulary and understanding necessary to make links between points in your answers. The skills you will build are to:

- acquire appropriate language to make links
- develop into explanations by making links between points
- show links between key aspects of the question to support your analysis.

In the exam, you will be asked to tackle questions such as the one below. This unit will prepare you to write your own response to this exam-style question.

Exam-style question

'Antiseptics were the biggest breakthrough in surgical treatment during the period c1800–c2000.'

How far do you agree? Explain your answer.

You may use the following in your answer:

- Joseph Lister
- chloroform.

You **must** also use information of your own.   (16 marks) + (4 marks)

The three key questions in the **skills boosts** will help you to identify and use linking phrases and to support your analysis by making links between supporting detail and the question.

① How do I know when to use linking phrases?

② How do I make links to develop my supporting knowledge?

③ How do I link my ideas and supporting detail back to the question?

Look at this student's first paragraph in response to the exam-style question on page 61.

> Antiseptics were a massive breakthrough in surgical treatments, as post-operative infection was one of the most common causes of death. This was especially the case after the development of effective anaesthetics, as surgeons were attempting longer and more complex operations. This increased the chances of infection setting in. Joseph Lister was a doctor who had read Pasteur's germ theory. It was not until he noticed the link between the smell on the ward and the smell of sewage that the use of carbolic acid during and after surgery was suggested. Lister tried using a carbolic spray in eleven surgeries, which all had successful, infection-free outcomes. He wrote about this in The Lancet, in the hope of encouraging other doctors to use carbolic spray as an antiseptic. Lister had proven that antiseptics could reduce deaths from infection. By 1900, Lister's methods were improved. Equipment was steamed and sterilised before use to prevent harmful bacteria being present in the operating theatre. This vastly reduced the risk of infection, going a long way to solving one of surgery's biggest problems.

① ⓐ Read the student's response carefully. Rewrite ✏ the narrative (supporting details) as a flow chart.

ⓑ Select an explanation link from the table and write ✏ its letter on each arrow, to show how the details have been linked together.

Explanation links
A ...Lister had proven...
B ...This increased the chances...
C ...in the hope of encouraging...
D It was not until...

Changes in surgical treatments, c1700–c1900

This unit uses the theme of changes in surgical treatments, c1700–c1900, to build your skills in making links between points. If you need to review your knowledge of this theme, work through these pages.

1 **a** Write 🖊 down the three main issues that existed in surgery at the start of the period c1700–c1900.

....

....

....

b Circle Ⓐ the two issues that were resolved by 1900.

2 **a** Put the following events describing the development of anaesthetics into chronological order by numbering 🖊 them from 1–6.

A **Nitrous oxide** was used as a recreational drug at 'gas parties'. People who injured themselves while 'under the influence' didn't immediately feel pain.	**D** Dr John Snow designed an inhaler to regulate the administering of **chloroform**, making it much safer to use.
B Surgeon James Simpson experimented with similar chemicals and created **chloroform**. However, it was difficult to control the dose a patient received.	**E** For centuries, doctors had experimented with herbs and chemicals that might prevent or reduce pain in surgery.
C Chemical **ether** was discovered in America and was used to make patients unconscious for operations. However, ether is highly flammable and irritated the lungs.	**F** Dental assistant Humphrey Davy was one of the first medical men to suggest using **nitrous oxide** (laughing gas) to numb pain during minor dental procedures.

b Explain 🖊 where in your event timeline (1–6) the issue of pain was resolved.

....

....

3 Look at the arguments in opposition to chloroform below. Write 🖊 the letters A–F in the relevant positions on the pyramid, to show which you think was the most and least influential argument.

A Anaesthetics took away the need for speed, which some surgeons saw as their main talent.	**B** Longer operations led to a greater risk of post-operative infection.	**C** It was thought that pain was sent by God and should be endured.
D The young, fit and fearful were most at risk of dying from an overdose of chloroform.	**E** It led some surgeons to try more risky operations, and this initially led to more deaths.	**F** Some surgeons found it useful to hear patients scream, as this meant they were still alive.

Most
influential

Least influential

Remember this?

4 Look at the stages in the development of antiseptics and aseptic conditions in surgery below.

> **A** In 1800 there were usually many people present during an operation, including 'dressers' to hold the patient still.

> **B** Joseph Lister read Pasteur's germ theory and noticed the smell of 'sewage' on the surgical ward. He successfully used cloths soaked in carbolic acid (used on sewage) on an infected operation wound.

> **C** Lister wrote about his successful work with carbolic acid in eleven surgical cases and published his findings in The Lancet.

> **D** Lister started to spray carbolic acid into the air during operations. It irritated the surgeons' skin when used in operations.

> **E** People remained sceptical as they could not explain Lister's success.

> **F** Surgical theatres became very wet when carbolic spray was used.

> **G** Lister focused on persuading doctors to use his spray, not trying to prove why it worked.

> **H** Other surgeons were inspired and began looking for better ways to perform aseptic surgery.

> **I** By 1900 theatres were scrubbed clean, instruments were steamed to kill germs, and rubber gloves, aprons and face masks were worn.

Write the letter of each stage in the correct column in the table below, to show whether it helped or hindered the fight against infection from surgery.

Helped	Hindered

5 Read the descriptions of twentieth-century advances in surgery arising from greater understanding of science and technology. Link each one to the type of surgery used to carry it out.

> **A** Enables the surgeon to carry out surgery which requires tiny blood vessel and nerve endings to be reattached. For example kidney transplants.

> **a** Micro surgery

> **B** Computers can work on a tiny scale, making tiny cuts and moving very precisely. This is of a particular advantage in brain surgery.

> **b** Laparoscopic (keyhole) surgery

> **C** Small incisions (cuts to enter the body) mean less trauma and a shorter recovery time.

> **c** Robotic surgery

1   How do I know when to use linking phrases?

Use linking phrases to avoid writing a list of 'what happened' and to ensure the knowledge you are describing supports your answer to the question. Linking phrases can also explain why someone does something (for example, 'in hope of...') or link a consequence back to the action ('as a result of...').

1 The table below gives some examples of cause and consequence linking phrases.

this meant that	this motivated	this led to
as a result	creating the potential to	in the hope of
this hindered	this contributed to	this influenced
increased the chances of	noticed the link between	it was not until

Circle Ⓐ those phrases used in the sample answer on page 62.

2 **a** Tick ✓ which of the following student responses uses linking phrases and so avoids writing a list of what happened.

b Now highlight 🖉 the linking phrases.

☐ Lister used carbolic spray in eleven surgeries. He wrote about it. Other doctors started to use carbolic spray.	☐ Lister tried using a carbolic spray in eleven surgeries, which all had successful, infection-free outcomes. He wrote about this in the medical journal *The Lancet*, in the hope of encouraging other doctors to use carbolic spray as an antiseptic.	☐ Lister used carbolic spray in eleven successful surgeries. He wrote about it in *The Lancet*. Other doctors read the article and started to use carbolic spray.

3 **a** Read the following passage. Rewrite 🖉 it below, but this time add some linking phrases, to link the description together. You can select phrases from the box in **1** to help.

> After the development of anaesthetics, surgeons were attempting longer and more complex operations. More people were dying from infection. Joseph Lister read Pasteur's germ theory. Joseph Lister also noticed the ward smelt like sewage. Carbolic acid was used on sewage to get rid of the smell. He suggested that carbolic acid was used during and after surgery.

....

....

....

....

....

b Some words have been highlighted in the original answer. Which of the following pronouns would you use for each of the highlighted words to avoid repetition: he, she, I, you, they, it, this, that, such? 🖉

Joseph Lister ....   carbolic acid ....

2 How do I make links to develop my supporting knowledge?

By linking rather than listing supporting details, you will start to develop your explanations. Think carefully about the meaning of each linking phrase and select the most appropriate to develop the point you are making.

(1) The following phrases can be used to build on detail used in your answer.

  a Circle (A) phrases to link causes and consequences.

  b Underline (A) phrases to link ideas about similarities.

In addition...	Furthermore...	Consequently...	Such as...
In contrast...	Evidence of...	For example...	Although...
In support of...	Similarly...	Equally important...	Made possible...
As a result of...	In spite of...	Compared to...	As well as...
Therefore...	Since...	Despite...	On the other hand...

(2) The two details below would make good supporting knowledge in a paragraph on the role of antiseptics in improving surgery (in response to the exam question on page 61).

  a Link (✏) the details by selecting a suitable linking phrase.

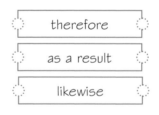

Joseph Lister published his findings in the medical journal The Lancet...

    therefore

    as a result

    likewise

... more doctors began to use carbolic spray during surgeries.

  b Try out the other linking phrases to complete the sentence. Does the linking phrase you have selected make a difference to the meaning or effectiveness of the sentence? If so, why? (✏)

....

....

(3) In this answer extract, the student wants to show that, although Lister's carbolic spray was not very popular, it did change people's attitudes towards how clean surgery was.

> Although Lister's carbolic spray was not very popular because it made things wet and irritated the skin, it led to a change in attitudes towards how clean surgery should be.

  a Circle (A) the linking phrase the student has used.

  b **i** Annotate (✏) the answer with some alternative linking phrases and then read the sentence with every option, to check which is best.

    ii Write (✏) your final choice of linking phrase below.

....

3 How do I link my ideas and supporting detail back to the question?

Different linking phrases will have different purposes in your writing, so it is important to be clear about what the question is asking you to do.

1. Complete ✏ the table by sorting the following linking phrases from the word box into the correct column to describe the purpose of the linking phrase.

such as	this motivated	however
as a result	whereas	in the hope of
this hindered	this contributed to	this influenced
increased the chances of	noticed the link between	in contrast

To compare and contrast ideas	To give examples of an idea	To show cause and effect
	For example...	

2. Your opening sentence of each paragraph should also be a linking phrase that makes it clear you intend to answer the question.

Tick ✓ the opening sentence below that most effectively addresses the question on page 61.

A ☐

Lister developed carbolic acid to be used as an antiseptic in surgery.

B ☐

One of the biggest breakthroughs in overcoming surgical problems in the period c1800–c2000 was Joseph Lister's use of carbolic acid as an antiseptic to reduce the risk of infection.

'How far do you agree' questions require you to write more than one paragraph, as you need to evaluate two opposing arguments and write a balanced response. By linking these two paragraphs you will produce a more effective answer.

3. a. In the opening sentence you ticked above, underline Ⓐ a phrase that shows the paragraph is agreeing with the statement.

b. Highlight ✏ the linking phrases in the table in ① that you might use to continue this paragraph and explain why Lister's use of carbolic acid shows antiseptics were the biggest breakthrough. Write ✏ your continuation below.

....

....

c. Highlight ✏ the linking phrases in the table in ① that would be appropriate ways to start a second paragraph arguing that antiseptics were **not** the biggest breakthrough in surgery. Remember to choose an opening sentence that clearly addresses the question.

Sample response

Use what you have learned in this unit to improve on the student's use of linking vocabulary in their response to this exam-style question.

Exam-style question

'Antiseptics were the biggest breakthrough in surgical treatments during the period c1800–c2000.'

How far do you agree? Explain your answer.

You may use the following in your answer:

- Joseph Lister
- chloroform.

You **must** also use your own information.

(16 marks) + (4 marks)

Antiseptics were a massive breakthrough in surgical treatments, as post-operative infection was one of the most common causes of death. This was especially the case after the development of effective anaesthetics, as surgeons were attempting longer and more complex operations. This increased the chances of infection setting in. Joseph Lister was a doctor who had read Pasteur's germ theory. It was not until he noticed the link between the smell on the ward and the smell of sewage that the use of carbolic acid during and after surgery was suggested. Lister tried using a carbolic spray in eleven surgeries, which all had successful, infection-free outcomes. He wrote about this in The Lancet, in the hope of encouraging other doctors to use carbolic spray as an antiseptic. Lister had proven that antiseptics could reduce deaths from infection. By 1900, Lister's methods were improved. Equipment was steamed and sterilised before use to prevent harmful bacteria being present in the operating theatre. This vastly reduced the risk of infection, going a long way to solving one of surgery's biggest problems.

1 Look at the student's first paragraph.

a Underline Ⓐ any phrases that link parts of the narrative (supporting details) to each other.

b Circle Ⓐ any phrases that link the narrative to the question being asked.

c Highlight ✏ one phrase used to make a link.

d Note down ✏ an alternative linking phrase you could use for the phrase you highlighted.

....

e Write ✏ why you think this would make a more appropriate choice for the point being made.

....
....
....
....

2 The student wants to make the counter argument that anaesthetics were a bigger breakthrough in their next paragraph. How would you start this paragraph? Write ✏ a full sentence to start the paragraph.

....
....
....

Your turn!

Now try this exam-style question using the skills you have built in this unit.

Exam-style question

'The use of chloroform was the key turning point in the development of surgery as an effective treatment in the years 1800 to the present day.'

How far do you agree? Explain your answer.

You may use the following information in your answer:

- James Simpson

- high-tech surgery.

You **must** also use information of your own.

(16 marks) + (4 marks)

(1) Use the following template to plan ✐ your answer.

Argument	Counter argument
Opening phrase	Opening phrase

Knowledge details to support this point:	Possible linking phrases:	Knowledge details to support this point:	Possible linking phrases:

Conclusion (remember to link back to the reasons you were most convinced by to explain your judgement):

Review your skills

Check up

Review your response to the exam-style question on page 69. Tick ✓ the column to show how well you think you have done each of the following.

	Had a go ✓	Nearly there ✓	Got it! ✓
considered the purpose of linking phrases and selected the most appropriate to support the point made	☐	☐	☐
selected a range of linking phrases to develop knowledge used rather than listing relevant details	☐	☐	☐
thought carefully about opening phrases that link effectively back to the question	☐	☐	☐

Need more practice?

You will need to practise what has been covered in this unit to answer all the other exam-style questions in this workbook. If you want to practise another exam-style question, try ✎ this one.

Exam-style question

'Individuals had the biggest impact on advances in treatment in the sixteenth and seventeenth centuries.'

How far do you agree? Explain your answer.

You may use the following in your answer:

- medical training
- the printing press.

You **must** also use information of your own.   (16 marks) + (4 marks)

How confident do you feel about each of these **skills**? Colour ✎ in the bars.

1 How do I know when to use linking phrases?	2 How do I make links to develop my supporting knowledge?	3 How do I link my ideas and supporting detail back to the question?
▢▢▢▢	▢▢▢▢	▢▢▢▢

⑧ Making a judgement

This unit will help you to make judgements and reach conclusions through prioritising of arguments and expressing evaluations.

The skills you will build are to:

- prioritise information to develop your analysis
- recognise and challenge generalisations
- move from the specific to the general without being overwhelmed by too many facts.

In the exam, you will be asked to tackle a question such as the one below. This unit will prepare you to write your own response to the question below.

Exam-style question

'The NHS was the most significant development in improving the treatment of illness in the nineteenth and twentieth centuries.'

How far do you agree? Explain your answer.

You may use the following in your answer:

- the NHS
- penicillin.

You **must** also use information of your own.

(16 marks) + (4 marks)

The three key questions in the **skills boosts** will help you prioritise details to reach an appropriate judgement.

 ① How do I organise information to reach a judgement?

 ② How do I make judgements?

 ③ How do I make a 'good' judgement?

Look at this student's plan and completed conclusion in response to the exam-style question on page 71.

Paragraph A: NHS
- Government investment in free healthcare for everyone in the UK
- Gave access to free treatments, so people could be treated regardless of cost/affordability
- Gave access to new treatments such as penicillin – saved lives of those who wouldn't have been able to afford newest treatments
- Offered cures and life improving/extending treatments
- Offered the latest surgical treatments
- Continues to invest in research
- Gave people access to high-tech diagnosis

Paragraph B: Penicillin
- First cure for general infection
- People no longer had to die if a simple infection set in, as they had in the past
- Inspired scientists to look for other antibiotics and other cures to diseases, e.g. cancer research, diabetes, HIV, etc.

Conclusion:
The NHS was the most influential development in treating disease, as without the NHS some people would be unable to afford treatments such as penicillin and would continue to die from simple infections. Even though the knowledge existed to cure them, they might seek cheaper, less effective remedies or do nothing. Antibiotics are significant progress in the fight against disease as cures, but the NHS has made these treatments, and others, available to the whole UK population.

(1) Complete ✐ the statement below based on what the student has written in their conclusion.

The student thinks that .... was the most significant development in the development of treatments and preventions in the twentieth century.

(2) How does the student justify their answer? Highlight ✐ the details in the student's conclusion that they use to support their judgement.

(3) The student plans to explain the significance of penicillin in the second paragraph. The NHS and penicillin are given in the question, which also asks for a third point of argument – 'information of your own'.

  (a) What development would you pick to compare to the NHS and penicillin, and why? ✐

  ....

  ....

  ....

  (b) Would your chosen development change the judgement in the student's conclusion? Why? ✐

  ....

  ....

  ....

The fight against disease

This unit uses the theme of the fight against disease to build your skills in making a judgement. If you need to review your knowledge of this theme, work through these pages.

① ⓐ Draw ✎ lines to link the description on the right to the correct 'stage of development' on the left.

A 1796: Jenner introduced the first vaccination programme. By the 1870s, Koch and Pasteur could explain how it worked.

a It was noticed that naturally occurring mould killed bacteria that caused blood poisoning. The mould was extracted and used to develop a general cure for infection.

B By 1914, Paul Ehrlich developed the first 'magic bullets'.

b Often made using a compound of coal tar (a by-product of industry). It worked the same way as stains to dye specific bacteria: seeking out particular bacteria in the body and killing just that bacteria, so the patient was cured of the disease but otherwise unharmed.

C 1928: Alexander Fleming discovered the first antibiotic (penicillin). By the 1940s, Florey and Chain could mass produce penicillin.

c A different or weakened form of a disease that, when introduced into the body, is not in a strong enough form to kill the patient but causes the body to make antibodies to fight the bacteria. This prevents the patient from contracting the disease if they come into contact with it again.

ⓑ Highlight ✎ the development that prevented disease rather than cured the patient.

② In your own words, explain ✎ the difference between prevention and cure.

....

....

③ Why were antibiotics, such as penicillin, an improvement on the early magic bullets? ✎

....

....

④ Why were some people opposed to vaccination? ✎

....

....

5. The table below contains a number of statements regarding the **treatment** and **prevention** of disease from 1900 to the present day.

a. Highlight ✏ treatments in one colour and preventions in another. Complete the key.

Key:

Treatments ▢　　　　　Preventions ▢

1 Research into gene therapy developed in the late twentieth century. ▢	2 People continue to buy 'over the counter' medications, but they are targeted at relieving specific symptoms rather than general remedies. ▢	3 The first successful transplant operation (kidney) was performed in 1956. Transplant operations are now performed regularly within the NHS. ▢
4 The First World War and the introduction of the NHS in 1948 led to an increase in specialisation among doctors. ▢	5 In the 1950s, the government passed the Clean Air Acts to reduce air pollution. In 2007 the government banned smoking in public places. ▢	6 The twentieth century saw many compulsory vaccination campaigns which attempted to eradicate diseases, such as the polio campaign of the 1950s and 1960s. ▢
7 In 1928 Fleming discovered the mould from which the first penicillin was extracted. ▢	8 At the start of the twentieth century, doctors were able to identify the specific bacteria causing a range of diseases. ▢	9 By the 1940s, Florey and Chain had discovered a way to mass produce penicillin. ▢
10 The NHS was introduced in 1948 as a free service for medical care for everyone. ▢	11 By 1914 the first medical cures had been developed. They were referred to as 'magic bullets' due to the way they worked. ▢	12 Technology such as X-rays and ultrasound scans make it easier for doctors to diagnose illness in patients. ▢
13 Other treatments such as radiotherapy and chemotherapy have proven successful in the treatment of cancer. ▢	14 Dialysis and heart bypass machines can buy a patient time while other treatments and cures are explored. ▢	15 The government now takes a much more proactive role in people's health with campaigns such as 'Stoptober' and 'Change4Life'. ▢

b. Tick ✓ any developments that were made more widely available by the NHS.

6. a. Select one development and explain its benefits: ✏ ....

....

....

b. Circle Ⓐ which of the following factors made this development possible:

technology　　government　　chance　　disease knowledge　　scientific investigation

How do I organise information to reach a judgement?

In your conclusions you will need to make a judgement. Before you can do this you need to have explored at least two different lines of argument. This skills boost aims to help you select which arguments to evaluate in order to reach a judgement.

Look again at the exam-style question below, taken from page 71. The highlighted section indicates the focus of the question, from which you will select your points of argument.

Exam-style question

'The NHS was the most significant development in improving the treatment of illness in the nineteenth and twentieth centuries.'

How far do you agree? Explain your answer.

You may use the following in your answer:

- the NHS
- penicillin.

You **must** also use information of your own.   (16 marks) + (4 marks)

① Below is a list of all the developments you may consider when answering this question. Remember, the NHS and penicillin are given to you in the question, so if you use both of these you will need to make a third point using details from your own knowledge.

A The NHS	B Penicillin	C Advanced diagnostics (e.g. X-rays)
D Anaesthetics for use in surgery	E Improvements in hospital care and hygiene	F Doctors specialise more

a Consider the significance of the impact of each of the above developments A–F on treating illness, then add 🖉 each letter to the chart below in the first column under whether you think they are most, less or least significant.

b Write 🖉 an explanation for your decisions in the spaces provided.

Most significant	This development had the biggest impact (significance) because
☐	....
	....
	....
Less significant	These two developments are less significant because ....
☐ ☐	....
	....
	But they are more significant than the three developments below.
Least significant	These are the least significant because ....
☐ ☐ ☐	....
	....
	....

The developments in rows 1 and 2 are the ones you will use in your answer, as they are the most significant. They are the arguments you will want to evaluate.

2 How do I make judgements?

When making a judgement it is helpful to consider the criteria by which you judge the **significance** of a factor or development. For example, you may be able to provide evidence that the NHS influenced medicine but how do you decide whether this was as significant as the impact of advances in technology?

1. Read student extracts A and B below. Each argues that a particular development (antibiotics or the NHS) was the most significant medical development. You may find the following measures of significance helpful when judging the impact of each factor.

> **Measures of significance**
>
> **Change** – How much changed/stayed the same?
>
> **Perception** – Did people at the time notice the impact?
>
> **Longevity** – Did this factor continue to have an impact for a long time?
>
> **Inspiration** – Did this factor cause other significant developments?
>
> **Scale** – Who was affected by this factor (locally, nationally, globally)?

a. Tick ✓ to indicate which measures of significance each student response uses.

A

> The discovery of penicillin was the most significant development of the twentieth century, as it was the first to cure disease. Before the development of penicillin, people frequently died from infections that would be unlikely to concern us today. Infection was a major issue in surgical procedures, and once infection took hold in the body it could not be stopped. Initially, penicillin was used to save wounded US soldiers during the Second World War; its success led to a global revolution in the fight against disease. Since this early development, scientists have gone on to discover new antibiotics, which are effective at targeting a wide range of infections.

Measure of significance ✓	A	Score	B ✓	Score
Change				
Perception				
Longevity				
Inspiration				
Scale				
Total score				

B

> The NHS is the most significant development in medicine in the twentieth century because it means everyone has equality of access to preventions and treatments. Before the NHS, people had to decide what treatments they could afford rather than receiving them as needed. As there was already National Health insurance that people could pay into, this mainly affected the unemployed – including the young and old. The NHS gave everybody in the UK access to life saving treatments such as penicillin without the worry of medical expenses. Moreover, the NHS now funds research and development into technologies and treatments, to ensure medicine continues to improve.

b. Which paragraph had more ticks for points of significance?

2. a. Repeat the task, but give each point of significance a score out of 5 for each paragraph, where 5 = very significant (biggest impact) and 0 = no significance (no tick).

b. Then total up each column. Record your findings.

3 How do I make a 'good' judgement?

You will know you have made a 'good' judgement if you are able to support your judgement with evidence that your selected argument is the most convincing – why is Argument X more significant than Argument Y if both are valid arguments?

1. Look at your final judgement for student responses A and B on page 76. Which scored the higher? Tick ✓ the reason why the extract scored more highly.

- Covered a wide range of measures of significance.

- Included one measure of significance that scored very highly.

The measures of significance will give the basis for the **support** you give for your judgement in your concluding paragraph.

2. a. To write a good answer to this type of exam question you must consider ideas beyond the two given in the question. Plan ✏ a third paragraph on another development significant in treating illness in the nineteenth and twentieth centuries (see the suggestions on page 75).

b. Look back at question 1 a on page 76 and the student response that you scored more highly. Highlight ✏ the sections in that paragraph that will be relevant to your concluding judgement.

3. a. Complete the conclusion paragraph below to produce a justified judgement. Remember to address the question in your conclusion so you need to make a comparison between the **NHS** and penicillin and/or your chosen third development. In the box below, circle Ⓐ the options that apply and write ✏ summaries to explain the significance.

> Overall I believe **penicillin / NHS /** .... was the most
> significant development in treatments of the 19th and 20th centuries because...
> A. it was significant in a range of areas such as ....
> ....
> or
> B. it was highly significant in that it... *changed medicine / people instantly benefitted / it continued to have an impact on medicine for generations / it caused further changes in medicine / it affected a large number of people. An example of how it was significant is*
> ....
> ....

b. An effective conclusion should meet the criteria below. Annotate ✏ your answer in the box above to show where you have attempted these criteria for your judgement to the penicillin / NHS argument.

Made a clear judgement	Compared the significance of developments

Justified your judgement	Made sure judgements and supporting details have already been mentioned – avoid introducing new ideas at this stage.

| Supported your judgement | |

Sample response

Look again at the student's plan on page 72 for answering the exam-style question on page 71. Now look at their plan for a third paragraph below.

> **Paragraph C: The use of anaesthetics in surgery**
> • Use of an effective pain relief enabled more complex surgeries.
> • Surgery became an effective solution to a great range of medical issues.

(1) You are now going to determine which of the following judgements (1–3), written by the student, gives the most effective judgement.

a Read the criteria (A–D) below and read the judgements (1–3). Tick ✓ the criteria boxes if the judgement has met the criterion.

Criteria:

A The judgement is made based on one of the three developments the student has suggested

B The judgement identifies what makes it significant (one detail / range of significance)

C The judgement and justification are supported with evidence

D The importance of the NHS is also considered, if not the main argument

Judgement	Criteria	✓
1. The effective use of pain relief in surgery has done far more to improve treatments. For example, effective pain relief has allowed surgeons to develop more complex surgeries to treat a wider range of medical issues.	A B C D	
2. The discovery of penicillin was a major breakthrough in the fight against disease and was the first success in finding a 'cure' rather than simply treating symptoms. It inspired a continuation in the fight and the development of further cures. We still use penicillin to treat infection to this day. This greatly improved the treatment of infections and similarly the effective use of pain relief greatly advanced surgical treatments. It suddenly opened up a whole new approach to treatments by making increasingly complex operations possible. However, by providing free health care, the NHS ensures that we have equality of access to both these areas of treatment and attempts to ensure no one goes untreated. The NHS also funds the continued development of both these areas of treatment. It is this that makes the NHS the most influential factor in improving treatments during the nineteenth and twentieth centuries.	A B C D	
3. I believe the NHS has been most important in developing treatments during the nineteenth and twentieth centuries, as it allows a large number of people to have equal access to free health care including treatments. Its impact also has longevity as it continues to influence treatments to this day. Despite being a major breakthrough, penicillin only really treats infection, so its impact is limited. Similarly pain relief only helped to improve surgical treatments. Therefore the NHS is overall the most influential factor in improving treatments.	A B C D	

b Circle Ⓐ which answer you think gives the best judgement.

| Judgement 1 | Judgement 2 | Judgement 3 |

Your turn!

Use some of the planning techniques you have learned to write an answer to the exam-style question below.

'The period c1800–present has been important mainly for finding preventions to disease.'
How far do you agree? Explain your answer.
You may use the following in your answer:

• vaccination programmes
• penicillin.

You **must** also use information of your own.   (16 marks) + (4 marks)

Note that, to plan a balanced response, you will need to consider both significant **prevention** as well as significant **treatment** to counter the argument.

① In the table below, write two new preventions and two new treatments. Below each, start to plan the arguments for it and note some judgements about the significance. ✐

> The measures of significance may help you: Change, Perception, Longevity, Inspiration and Scale. See page 76 for detail on them.

Prevention 1:	Treatment 1:
Arguments:	Arguments:
Judgements about significance:	Judgements about significance:
Prevention 2:	Treatment 2:
Arguments:	Arguments:
Judgements about significance:	Judgements about significance:

② **a** Complete ✐ the table below to rank the significance of your arguments in ①. Make sure you include preventions **and** treatments.

Most significant	This development had the biggest impact (significance) on prevention or treatments because ....
Less significant	These developments are less significant because .... But they are more significant than the developments below.
Least significant	These are the least significant because ....

b Overall, which do you think has been more significant since 1800: prevention or treatment? Circle ✐ your judgement.

③ Now write ✐ either the whole answer or a conclusion with a justified judgement on a separate sheet of paper.

Review your skills

Check up

Review your response to the exam-style question on page 79. Tick ✓ the column to show how well you think you have done each of the following.

	Had a go ✓	Nearly there ✓	Got it! ✓
selected relevant and significant points of argument, ensuring they covered both sides of the question	☐	☐	☐
explained the significance of each point of the argument	☐	☐	☐
reached a judgement in the conclusion, which identified the point of argument believed to be most significant	☐	☐	☐
justified the judgement made using the criteria for judging significance and based on ideas and details explained in the paragraphs	☐	☐	☐

Need more practice?

You will need to practise what has been covered in this unit to answer other exam-style questions in this workbook. If you want to practise another question, try 🖉 this one:

Exam-style question

'Technology has had the biggest impact on advances in treatment in the period since 1800.'

How far do you agree? Explain your answer.

You may use the following in your answer:

* X-rays
* robotic surgery.

You **must** also use information of your own.

(16 marks) + (4 marks)

How confident do you feel about each of these **skills**? Colour 🖉 in the bars.

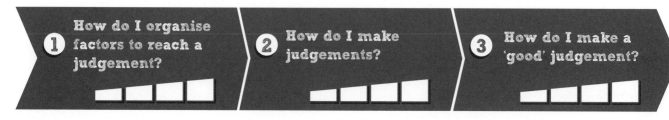

1 How do I organise factors to reach a judgement?

2 How do I make judgements?

3 How do I make a 'good' judgement?

Answers

Unit 1

Page 2

① and **②** During the battle for Arras the British and Commonwealth troops used the existing Roman quarries, to launch a surprise attack on the Germans. This meant there was less work to prepare the position of attack and less chance of soldiers being injured through collapse. The quarries also open up into large caverns where the chalk was removed from the ground to be used during the Middle Ages. This meant that soldiers were not confined in cramped conditions and there was even space for a fully functioning hospital where soldiers could be treated and operated on quickly after injury. ~~The quicker a wounded soldier could be treated the more chance they had of survival.~~

③ **a** There was less work to prepare the position of attack and less chance of soldiers being injured through collapse.

b There was space for a fully functioning hospital meaning soldiers could be operated on quickly.

Page 3

① Tick: **b** and **d**

②

Feature of trench system	Description on artwork
Reserve trench	A trench around 100m behind the support trench. A place where reserve troops could wait in case the front line was taken by enemy forces.
Frontline trench	A trench from which attacks would be made. Soldiers would leave the trench system here to 'go over the top'.
Communication trench	A trench running between trench lines in order to communicate orders.
Support trench	A line of trenches for frontline soldiers to retreat (move back) to if necessary during an attack.
Dugouts	Places in the sides of trenches to give soldiers extra protection when needed.
Artillery emplacements	An area behind all lines of trenches. Shells would be fired over the trenches at enemy lines and soldiers would be protected during the creeping barrage.

Page 4

③ less chance of collapse

room to create an underground hospital

large, well-ventilated spaces

Page 4 (right column)

④ A to c

B to b

C to a

⑤ **a** **Trench fever:** Lice and other pests who lived in trenches

b **Trench foot:** Constantly wet and muddy conditions

c **Shell shock:** Frequent shelling and exposure to danger

d **Gas exposure:** Gasses being trapped in trenches below ground level

Page 5

① A: "transportation of wounded soldiers from the Front Line."

B: "trench environment which were unhealthy"

② **a**

Question A	Question B
Horses were used to transport wounded soldiers to CCSs.	Pests such as lice and rats were a common problem, infesting the trenches and men's uniforms.
Stretcher bearers collected the wounded men from no-man's land.	Trenches were often saturated by rain and very muddy or filled with water.

b Student's own response.

Page 6

① A to c

B to a

C to d

D to b

② Student's own response.

Page 7

① Question A: Describe **two** features of transportation of wounded soldiers from the Front Line.

Question B: Describe **two** features of the trench environment which were unhealthy.

Sentence 1 (feature 1)	Horses were used to transport wounded soldiers to CCSs.
Sentence 2 (supporting detail)	Although horses were considered too slow and struggled to cope with the large numbers of wounded soldiers, they did not break down in the muddy conditions so continued to be used.
Sentence 3 (feature 2)	Stretcher bearers collected the wounded men from no-man's-land.
Sentence 4 (supporting detail)	It was only possible to collect the wounded from no-man's-land using men carrying stretchers but they had to perform their duties under very dangerous conditions and risked becoming wounded themselves.

Sentence 1 (feature 1)	Trenches were often saturated by rain and very muddy or filled with water.
Sentence 2 (supporting detail)	This often caused a condition called trench foot, which is when the blood supply to the foot is lost and the skin begins to decompose.
Sentence 3 (feature 2)	Pests such as lice and rats were a common problem, infesting the trenches and men's uniforms.
Sentence 4 (supporting detail)	It was discovered that the lice carried a disease that caused the soldiers to suffer from flu-like symptoms. This illness was called trench fever.

Page 8

> The support trenches were about eighty metres behind the frontline trenches. They were where additional men and supplies could be kept in case of an attack on the Front Line. The communication trenches ran between the lines of trenches to allow messages and supplies to be transported backwards and forwards between the lines. Conditions were safer in the support trenches than the front line as they were not within range of enemy snipers.

1. Feature 1 and supporting detail = yellow; Feature 2 and supporting detail = green.
2. 4/4
3. Final circled sentence is not relevant.
4. Feature: Student's own response.

   Supporting detail: Student's own response.

Page 9

1. "features of the dugout"
2. , 3. , and 4. Student's own response.

Unit 2

Page 12

1. Student's own response.

Page 13

1. (a) Medical officers, stretcher bearers, or medical orderlies.

   (b) Driving patients in ambulance wagons, providing baths with heated water via vans, setting up cinemas or driving food supplies and clothing to the Front Line.

2. (a) From the Front Line = 1 Regimental Aid Post – 2 Advanced and Main Dressing Stations – 3 Casualty Clearing Stations – 4 Base Hospitals.

   (b) A to c

      B to a

      C to d

      D to b

Page 14

3. (a) Mobile X-ray units, Thomas splint, blood transfusion, plastic surgery, or amputation.

(b) Blood transfusion
(c) Brain surgery
(d) Amputation

4. (a) X-ray = Yellow   Blood loss = Green
   (b)

Extremely fragile imaging equipment was difficult to move.	It was known that type O blood was a universal donor which could safely be given to anyone.
Difficult to keep blood fresh when transporting it to patients, as it could not be refrigerated.	Adding sodium citrate to donated blood prevented clotting and meant it could be stored for longer.
Images did not detect certain materials or debris in wounds, such as fragments of clothing, which could cause infection if not removed.	Units were set up in tents next to the van which carried the fragile imaging equipment.
If a patient was given the wrong blood type, they might suffer a serious reaction.	Mobile units were only used for emergency detection of shrapnel. Better-quality images could be taken at base hospitals.

Page 15

1. Controlling blood loss and general care, both acceptable answers.
2. and 3. Student's own response.

Page 16

1. Anaesthetics:

   I spent most of my time giving anaesthetics...

   If they had to wait their turn in the normal way until the surgeon was able to perform the operation with a doctor giving the anaesthetic, it would have been too late for many of them.

   Surgery:

   It was a question of operating as quickly as possible.

   If they had to wait their turn in the normal way until the surgeon was able to perform the operation with a doctor giving the anaesthetic, it would have been too late for many of them.

   Untrained medical staff:

   I had no right to be doing this because I had no medical qualifications...

   If they had to wait their turn in the normal way until the surgeon was able to perform the operation with a doctor giving the anaesthetic, it would have been too late for many of them.

Evacuation process:

...the journey from the battlefield was simply terrible for these poor lads.

(2) Student's own response.

Page 17

(1) treating wounded soldiers

(2), (3), (4), and (5) Student's own response.

Page 18

(1) I spent most of my time giving anaesthetics...

If they had to wait their turn in the normal way, until the surgeon was able to perform the operation with a doctor giving the anaesthetic, it would have been too late for many of them.

(2) Alternative questions:

'How often did people without medical experience give anaesthetics?'

'What were the dangers/potential issues of people without medical training giving anaesthetics?'

Knowledge:

'Anaesthetics were an important development in preventing the body going into shock, so it was important that it was given early.'

(3) and (4) Student's own response.

Page 19

Student's own response.

Unit 3

Page 22

(1) (a) ...as it tells the historian about the effect of chlorine gas on someone who has been exposed. It describes the effect on the lungs as like drowning, which is because chlorine gas caused irritation that led to fluid building up in the lungs and possible suffocation. It also describes symptoms such as headaches and chest pain.... as a soldier writing about the effects of gas, he had first-hand experience of witnessing these symptoms and the fact that these are notes taken at the time make this account more useful to the historian, as he is describing what he is seeing rather than remembering these facts.

(b) Though Cotton speaks about cases he has witnessed, it's unclear whether these symptoms, followed by death, were typical of all soldiers exposed to chlorine gas. Also, the provenance does not say that Lance Sergeant Elmer Cotton had any medical training, which may mean he is less able to accurately identify medical symptoms.

(c) Also, the provenance does not say that Lance Sergeant Elmer Cotton had any medical training, which may mean he is less able to accurately identify medical symptoms.

(d) which is because chlorine gas caused irritation that led to fluid building up in the lungs and possible suffocation.

Page 23

(1) Shrapnel

(2) (a) i Morphine – pain relief to make wounded soldier comfortable

ii Haemorrhage – blood loss

iii Dressing – to clean and bandage the wound in the first instance

iv Tetanus – a type of infection or disease that got into wounds from soil

v Septic – infected wound

(b) Infection

(3)

To prevent severity	To prevent infection
The Brodie helmet was introduced in 1915. This was a steel helmet with a strap that prevented it being thrown off the head in an explosion.	'Gas gangrene', which could be caused by bacteria in the soil, could affect wounds and spread rapidly. Infected limbs could be amputated.
The impact of tetanus was reduced by the use of anti-tetanus injections from the end of 1914.	In the late 19th century, Hugh Thomas, in his medical practice, had designed a splint to stop joints from moving called the Thomas Splint.

Page 24

(4) (a) A to b

B to c

C to a

(b) Urinating on pieces of cloth.

(5) (a) Shell shock: psychological disorder arising from prolonged exposure to warfare, especially bombardment.

Trench fever: highly contagious disease caused by lice that infested soldiers in the trenches in the First World War.

Trench foot: extremely painful foot condition due to long periods of immersion in cold water and mud, leading to the death of skin and tissue.

(b) A to e, g

B to a

C to b, c, f

Page 25

(1) What were the chances of a wound becoming infected? ("..they should be more sanitary and hygienic in their nature.")

How were infections treated? ("...they should be much better equipped with operating theatres and other appliances...")

In what conditions were soldiers treated? ("...that they should be much better equipped with operating theatres and other appliances, and that they should be more sanitary and hygienic in their nature.")

(2) What are the nature of the wounds? (Photo shows one soldier with a head bandage which may have been caused by shrapnel.)

In what conditions were soldiers treated?
(Photo shows soldiers with warm coats, clean boots in the large gardens of a house, with a team of nursing staff. Conditions appear to be good.)

Page 26

(1) and (2) Student's own response.

Page 27

(1) and (2) Student's own response.

Page 28

(1) Identifies content that is useful from Source A

Identifies content that is useful from Source B

Identifies an element of provenance that may limit how the source is used

(2) Identifies content that is useful from Source A – "…it implies that wounds were not being treated quickly enough. It also implies that there is a great need for well-equipped operating theatres, which suggests that surgery was used to treat wounds."

Identifies content that is useful from Source B – "…a photograph of wounded soldiers so it is useful in showing us the possible consequences of wounds and gives an accurate and reliable example of amputations."

Identifies an element of provenance that may limit how the source is used – "A politician gave the speech in Source A in 1915; he had no first-hand experience and was relying on what other people told him. He might also be emphasising the negative aspects of wound treatment, to persuade the government to increase spending in this area."

Unit 4

Page 32

(1) Explain one way in which people's beliefs about the causes of disease were the same in the nineteenth century as they were during the seventeenth century.

(2) During the nineteenth century people continued to believe strongly in…

This is a continuation in beliefs from the seventeenth century…

This fitted in with the earlier belief that…

(3) …the link between them and disease was not proven until Pasteur's germ theory in 1861…

(4) During the nineteenth century people continued to believe strongly in…

This is a continuation in beliefs from the seventeenth century…

This fitted in with the earlier belief that…

Page 33

(1) Underline: Middle Ages, supernatural, scientific, rational

(2) A to c

B to d

C to e

D to g

E to f

F to b

G to a

Page 34

(3) a and b   Rational   Supernatural

Four Humours	Miasma	Punishment from God
Blood not used up and replaced (Harvey)	Clinical observations key to understanding disease (Sydenham)	Animalcules (Royal Society publication)
Dissections to better understand the body	Evil spirits	Astrology (impact of the position of stars and planets)

(4)

Factor of influence	New ideas
Scientific discovery	Animalcules, blood not used up
Understanding of anatomy	Dissections, blood not used up
Questioning of the Church	In a way all are alternatives considered due to increased questioning of the Church
Suggestions by key individuals, e.g. Thomas Sydenham	Animalcules, blood not used up
New technology such as Leeuwenhoek's microscope	Animalcules

(5) New religious ideas questioned the power of the Catholic Church. This made it more difficult for the Church to put forward its ideas about science. Although people were still religious, they were more prepared to look for different explanations for why diseases occurred. People began to believe that disease was not caused by God.

Page 35

(1) 1200: 13th century   1300: 14th century
1500: 16th century

1600: 17th century   1700: 18th century
1800: 19th century

1900: 20th century   2000: 21st century

(2) fourteenth and seventeenth centuries

(3) people's beliefs about the causes of disease

(4) were different in the nineteenth century and the seventeenth century

(5) - Fourteenth and seventeenth centuries

- People's reactions to the plague in Britain

- were similar in the fourteenth and seventeenth centuries

- nineteenth century… sixteenth century

- people's beliefs about the causes of disease

- were different in the nineteenth century to the sixteenth century

- nineteenth century... seventeenth century

- people's beliefs about the causes of disease

- were different in the nineteenth century and the seventeenth century

Page 36

① - seventeenth century... thirteenth century

- people's beliefs about the causes of disease

- were the same in the seventeenth century as they were in the thirteenth century

② A, D, E

③ **a** outside of question time parameters

b about change not continuity during the Renaissance

c outside of question time parameters AND about change not continuity during the Renaissance AND about treatments rather than beliefs about the causes of disease

Page 37

① Tick:

Identified one difference?

Selected content knowledge for that difference for the first time period required?

Selected content knowledge for that difference for the second time period required?

Do not tick:

Explained how there is a similarity or a difference? – They need a more direct comparison to fully explain the difference, i.e. 'The development of antibiotics mean far fewer people die from infection today.'

② "...are different today from the nineteenth century is that we can now cure infections using antibiotics...."

③ Student's own response.

Page 38

① Time period: seventeenth century and fourteenth century

Topic/theme: people's beliefs about the causes of disease

Comparison: were the same in the seventeenth century as they were in the fourteenth century

② In the seventeenth century people still believed in God...

...fewer people believed that God sent disease...

...bad smells still fitted with these ideas, so people and doctors continued to use them as an explanation for disease

...idea was developed when animalcules were discovered but the principle was the same...

③ **a** ... people became more concerned with external factors causing disease...

...fewer people believed that God sent disease...

b Student's own response.

④ Student's own response.

Page 39

① **a** seventeenth century and fourteenth century

b people's beliefs about the causes of disease

②, **③**, **④**, and **⑤** Student's own response.

Page 42

① "Because people didn't have scientific explanations for the causes of disease, they still believed that it was a punishment sent by God for their sins. People continued to follow the advice of the Church regarding illness and often used prayer and repentance as a way of preventing disease."

"The Theory of the Four Humours fitted well with the Church, so the Church supported it..."

"Doctors continued to use Galen's theory of opposites to restore the balance of the humours in their patients. Bloodletting and purges remained common treatments for illness."

② Student's own response.

Unit 5

Page 43

①

Astrology – symptoms and diseases were affected by the movement of the stars and planets.	People didn't want to risk going to Hell so they listened to what the Church told them. They made an effort to live a sin-free life, prayed and acted upon any penances (punishments) the priests gave them. Flagellation (whipping yourself) was a common self-punishment.	The Theory of the Four Humours stated that illness occurred when the body's four liquids (humours) were out of balance. Ancient doctors had observed that the world was made up of four elements and four seasons so it followed that the body must have four humours and this linked to disease.
People believed that lepers (people with the skin disease leprosy) had sinned and the disease was a sign of their sin. There was no cure and they were usually banished from the community.	Malnutrition – people believed that God punished people by sending famines. People who survived them believed God had forgiven them through prayer.	Miasma was the belief that evil fumes could contaminate the air. Bad smells were believed to be an indication of air that contained disease.
Galen wrote the Theory of the Four Humours and the Theory of Opposites to treat imbalance.	The balance of the body could be controlled through diet, bloodletting and purging (vomiting).	In the later Middle Ages doctors were trained at universities to use clinical observations and the Four Humours, following the teachings of Hippocrates and Galen.

② Student's own response.

Page 44

③ and ④ Superstitions and faith

Herbal

Four Humours

Pilgrimage	Fasting	Prayer/Mass
A journey to an important religious monument, shrine or place. To gain forgiveness for sins	Going without food. Self punishment to prevent God's punishment	Healing prayers and incantations (spells) To gain forgiveness for sins
The king's touch	**Nothing**	**Astrology**
It was widely believed that the king had the power to heal certain illnesses because of his 'divine right'. This was considered particularly effective for scrofula. King chosen by God	Occasionally people were discouraged from seeking cures. If God had sent the disease to purge the soul, it was important for the disease to run its course. God's choice	Position of the stars and planets was used to write a horoscope as these were used to diagnose and suggest treatments. Position of planets dictated fate
Bloodletting	**Purging**	**Clyster**
Phlebotomy or bloodletting was about removing excess blood from the body through a cut or using leeches. Blood one of the four humours – bring humours back into balance	Clearing the digestive system of 'bad food', either by taking a laxative to cause bowel movements or taking a purgative to make you vomit. To balance the humours	Like an enema – used to wash out your bowels. To balance the humours
Drinks	**Food**	**Bathing**
People would drink herbal infusions. Often the recommended ingredients were very expensive. Herbs which were known to relieve symptoms	Commonly included spicy, warming foods such as ginger, pepper and cardamom. Herbs which were known to relieve symptoms	Hot baths to steam out impurities and administer herbal remedies. *Regimen Sanitatis* was a set of ideas about hygiene. Herbs which were known to relieve symptoms

Page 45

① (a) the causes of disease

(b) c1250–c1500

(c) explain why there was little change in ideas

② (a) Cross out: Herbal remedies through drinks and baths

(b) Cross out: Scientists had identified animalcules in the air

(c) All remaining fit the concept.

(d) Left with: Malnutrition, Punishment for sins, The Theory of the Four Humours

Page 46

① (a) There was continuity in beliefs about the causes of disease during the Middle Ages <u>because physicians continued to read the works of ancient doctors such as Galen</u>. Galen was a doctor in Ancient Rome who wrote about the Theory of the Four Humours. This was a rational theory about the cause of disease first developed by the Ancient Greeks. It was based on the belief that disease was caused by an imbalance of bodily fluids or 'humours'. It was linked to the world being created in fours – four seasons, four elements etc... <u>As the Church supported the logic behind the theory, physicians were trained by reading Galen's work and they continued to use the Theory of the Four Humours to explain disease</u>.

(b) Doctors were trained using Galen's books.

The rational ideas were accepted by the Church.

② and ③ Student's own response.

Page 47

① Cross out

- People didn't want to risk going to Hell, so they listened to what the Church told them.

- The Four Humours

- People believed that lepers had sinned and their skin disease was a sign of their sin.

- Galen wrote about the Theory of the Four Humours.

- In the later Middle Ages, universities trained doctors to use clinical observations and the Four Humours, following the teachings of Hippocrates and Galen.

② Student's own response.

Page 48

① (a) The Church was very influential in the continuity of ideas about the causes of disease during the Middle Ages...

People continued to follow the advice of the Church regarding illness...

Furthermore, the Theory of the Four Humours fitted well with the teachings of the Church, so the Church supported the theory...

The Church also banned dissection, so doctors and surgeons were reliant on the anatomical teachings of Galen…

Finally, people continued to believe that the air had something to do with the spread of disease….

As the cause of disease could not be seen, people in the Middle Ages continued to believe it might be in the air. For this reason the rational explanation of miasma – bad air – continued to be used.

b Romans had avoided building their homes near swamps and other features that emitted bad smells, due to the belief that these bad smells were an indication of and commonly present with disease.

c Because people didn't have scientific explanations for the cause of disease…

People continued to follow the advice of the Church…

…the Theory of the Four Humours fitted well with the teachings of the Church…

Doctors continued to use Galen's Theory of Opposites…

Finally, people continued to believe that the bad air had something to do with the spread of disease.

As the cause of disease could not be seen…

d Finally, people continued to believe that the air had something to do with the spread of disease. Romans had avoided building their homes near swamps and other features that emitted bad smells, due to the belief that these bad smells were an indication of and commonly present with disease. As the cause of disease could not be seen, people in the Middle Ages continued to believe it might be in the air. For this reason the rational explanation of miasma – bad air – continued to be used.

(2) Spontaneous generation | Germ Theory

Early alternative to the Four Humours	Microbes **caused** matter to decay.	Decaying matter **produces** microbes rather than **causing** the decay	Microbes produced once an animal or plant had died or had started rotting	Microbes could cause death or rotting process by increasing in number (germinating)	Microbes cannot survive in sterile conditions and can be killed using heat

(3) Koch used coal tar products to invent a stain that would colour specific bacteria and identify them without killing the patient.

Page 54

(4) J, F, E, A, C, K, B, I, D, H, G,

(5) change | continuity

Nightingale wards with hand washing, clean bedding and controlled diet.	Carbolic soap and carbolic acid were used to clean hospital environments.	Many people were still treated at home by family members for most illnesses.	Treatments were bought from apothecaries.
Quack or 'patent remedies' still very popular.	Pasteur and Koch had discovered bacteria for a number of diseases and could create a weakened strain to be used as a vaccine.	The government started to take responsibility for sanitary conditions, introducing two public health Acts and a sewer system in London.	Edward Jenner discovered a vaccine for small pox by using cow pox, a less serious disease which created the same antibodies.
The development of anaesthetics and antiseptics improved surgical outcomes.	Blood loss was still an issue in surgical procedures.	Antiseptics were a prevention to infection but not a cure once infection during surgical treatment set in.	Some people opposed vaccination and anaesthetics on the grounds that they interfered with God's will.

(1) Topic/theme: how illness was prevented and treated

Time parameters: c1250–c1500

Concept: Explain why there was very little change

(2) and (2) Student's own response.

Unit 6

Page 52

(1) a Paragraphs 1 and 3

b Paragraph 2

(2) Student's own response.

Page 53

(1) The Church was becoming less important in people's lives = **People were willing to accept alternatives to the idea of disease being a punishment from God.**

Cities were begin to grow so finding a cause to the increasing risk of disease became a priority = **Scientists had the motivation to come up with new theories and material to observe.**

Theories such of the Four Humours were abandoned as it was increasingly apparent treatments in response didn't work = **If this rational idea was not providing treatments which worked maybe they need to look for alternative rational causes.**

The use of microscopes to further study microbes – 'animalcules' = **These technologies allowed scientists to study the world in more detail than ever before.**

(6) Student's own choice but could argue that surgical treatments changed rapidly as a result of knowledge and preventions (i.e. vaccinations), but the cures did not increase despite knowledge.

Page 55

(1) a events change

In 1861 Louis Pasteur published his germ theory, criticising the theory of spontaneous generation.	In 1882 Robert Koch discovered the bacteria which caused tuberculosis.	From their reading of Pasteur's germ theory, doctors began to alter their understanding of human disease. Based on Pasteur's descriptions of reducing bacteria by heating liquids and halting the decaying process by keeping matter in an sterile environment, practices began to change.
Scientists such as Louis Pasteur were inspired to study the behaviour of microorganisms and test theories such as spontaneous generation. Through experimentation they realised the old theories were wrong and developed new explanations that stood up to testing.	In 1668 Leeuwenhoek developed the microscope which allowed study into the behaviour of microorganisms.	A study of the bacteria that caused tuberculosis along with studies of other identified bacteria led to a series of vaccines being created. This meant a number of serious diseases in humans were now preventable.

b 1861 Louis Pasteur published his germ theory, criticising the theory of spontaneous generation.	→	From their reading of Pasteur's germ theory, doctors began to alter their understanding of human disease. Based on Pasteur's descriptions of reducing bacteria by heating liquids and halting the decaying process by keeping matter in an sterile environment, practices began to change.
In 1882 Robert Koch discovered the bacteria which caused tuberculosis.	→	A study of the bacteria that caused tuberculosis along with studies of other identified bacteria led to a series of vaccines being created. This meant a number of serious diseases in humans were now preventable.
In 1668 Leeuwenhoek developed the microscope which allowed study into the behaviour of microorganisms.	→	Scientists like Louis Pasteur were inspired to study the behaviour of microorganisms and test theories such as spontaneous generation. Through experimentation they realised the old theories were wrong and developed new explanations that stood up to testing.

Page 56

(1) a Industrial Revolution

b Renaissance

c Industrial Revolution

d Middle Ages or Renaissance

(2) Student's own response.

Page 57

(1) a Immediate impact:

C, D

Impact on ideas:

A, E, F, G

Widespread impact:

A, D, E, F

On-going impact:

A, B, F, H

Long-term impact:

A, B, D, F

b G

c Student's own response.

Page 58

(1) Student's own response.

Page 59

Student's own response.

Unit 7

Page 62

(1) a , b Antiseptics were a massive breakthrough in surgical treatments, as post-operative infection was one of the most common causes of death. This was especially the case after the development of effective anaesthetics, as surgeons were attempting longer and more complex operations.

B – This increased the chances…

… of infection setting in. Joseph Lister was a doctor who had read Pasteur's germ theory.

D – It was not until…

…he noticed the link between the smell on the ward and the smell of sewage that the use of carbolic acid during and after surgery was suggested. Lister tried using a carbolic spray in eleven surgeries, which all had successful, infection-free outcomes. He wrote about this in The Lancet,

C – in the hope of encouraging…

…other doctors to use carbolic spray as an antiseptic.

A – Lister had proven…

… that antiseptics could reduce deaths from infection. By 1900, Lister's methods were improved. Equipment was steamed and sterilised before use to prevent harmful bacteria being present in the operating theatre. This vastly reduced the risk of infection, going a long way to solving one of surgery's biggest problems.

Page 63

(1) (a) **1** Blood loss   **2** Infection   **3** Pain (in any order)

(b) Infection and pain

(2) (a) E, A, F, C, B, D

(b) Student's own response.

(3) Student's own response.

Page 64

(4)

Helped	Hindered
B, C, H, I	A, D, E, F, G

(5) A to **a**

B to **c**

C to **b**

Page 65

(1) Increased the chances of

Noticed the link between

In the hope of

(2) (a) Middle answer

(b) , which

, in the hope of

(2) (a) Student's own response.

(b) He (Joseph Lister) it/this/such (carbolic acid)

Page 66

(1) (a) As a result of…

Therefore…

Consequently…

Made possible…

(b) In addition…

In support of…

Furthermore…

Similarly…

Since…

For example…

Equally important…

Compared to…

Such as…

As well as…

(2) (a) 'as a result' or 'therefore'

(b) 'therefore' and 'as a result' imply that because he published his findings, doctors began to use carbolic spray. 'likewise' implies that the two events occurred at the same time, but there was no link.

(3) (a) it led to

(b) Student's own response.

Page 67

(1) To compare and contrast ideas: in contrast…, whereas…, however…

To give examples of an idea: For example…, such as…

To show cause and effect: as a result…, this hindered…, increased the chances of…, this motivated…, this contributed to…, noticed the link between…, in the hope of…, this influenced…,

(2) Sentence B

(3) (a) "One of the biggest breakthroughs in overcoming surgical problems in the period c1800–c2000 was…"

(b) Student's own response.

(c) Based on student's own knowledge, but could have '…noticed the link between…' (smell of sewage and smell on post-operative wards). 'It was not until…' (Lister made the connection between post-operative infection and germ theory).

Page 68

(1) (a) Antiseptics were a massive breakthrough in surgical treatments, as post-operative infection was one of the most common causes of death. This was especially the case after the development of effective anaesthetics, as surgeons were attempting longer and more complex operations. This increased the chances of infection setting in. Joseph Lister was a doctor who had read Pasteur's germ theory. It was not until he noticed the link between the smell on the ward and the smell of sewage that the use of carbolic acid during and after surgery was suggested. Lister tried using a carbolic spray in eleven surgeries, which all had successful, infection-free outcomes. He wrote about this in The Lancet, in the hope of encouraging other doctors to use carbolic spray as an antiseptic. Lister had proven that antiseptics could reduce deaths from infection. By 1900, Lister's methods were improved. Equipment was steamed and sterilised before use to prevent harmful bacteria being present in the operating theatre. This vastly reduced the risk of infection, going a long way to solving one of surgery's biggest problems.

(b) Antiseptics were a massive breakthrough in surgical treatments, as post-operative infection was one of the most common causes of death. This was especially the case after the development of effective anaesthetics, as surgeons were attempting longer and more complex operations. This increased the chances of infection setting in. Joseph Lister was a doctor who had read Pasteur's germ theory. It was not until he noticed the link between the smell on the ward and the smell of sewage that the use of carbolic acid during and after surgery was suggested. Lister tried using a carbolic spray in eleven surgeries, which all had successful, infection-free outcomes. He wrote about this in 'The Lancet', in the hope of encouraging other doctors to use carbolic spray as an antiseptic. Lister had proven that antiseptics could reduce deaths from infection. By 1900, Lister's methods were improved. Equipment was steamed and sterilised before use to prevent harmful bacteria being present in the operating theatre. This vastly reduced the risk of infection, going a long way to solving one of surgery's biggest problems.

c Antiseptics were a massive breakthrough in surgical treatments, as post-operative infection was one of the most common causes of death. This was especially the case after the development of effective anaesthetics, as surgeons were attempting longer and more complex operations. This increased the chances of infection setting in. Joseph Lister was a doctor who had read Pasteur's germ theory. It was not until he noticed the link between the smell on the ward and the smell of sewage that the use of carbolic acid during and after surgery was suggested. Lister tried using a carbolic spray in eleven surgeries, which all had successful, infection-free outcomes. He wrote about this in 'The Lancet', in the hope of encouraging other doctors to use carbolic spray as an antiseptic. Lister had proven that antiseptics could reduce deaths from infection. By 1900, Lister's methods were improved. Equipment was steamed and sterilised before use to prevent harmful bacteria being present in the operating theatre. This vastly reduced the risk of infection, going a long way to solving one of surgery's biggest problems.

d and e Student's own response.

2 Student's own response.

Page 69

Student's own response.

Unit 8

Page 72

1 the NHS

2 ...without the NHS some people would be unable to afford treatments such as penicillin and would continue to die from simple infections.

...the NHS has made these treatments, and others, available to the whole UK population.

3 Student's own response.

Page 73

1 a A to c
      B to b
      C to a

   b Highlight: A

2 Student's own response but for example:
Prevention has to be used before contracting a disease and teaches the body's immune system to fight off a specific disease. Cure can be given after the disease has been contracted and acts instead of or alongside the body to fight the disease or infection.

3 Antibiotics are an improvement on magic bullets as they cure general infection rather than specific diseases.

4 Student's own response.

Page 74

5 a and b Treatments   Preventions

1 Research into gene therapy developed in the late twentieth century. ✓	2 People continue to buy 'over the counter' medications, but they are targeted at relieving specific symptoms rather than general remedies.	3 The first successful transplant operation (kidney) was performed in 1956. Transplant operations are now performed regularly within the NHS. ✓
4 The First World War and the introduction of the NHS in 1948 led to an increase in specialisation among doctors. ✓	5 In the 1950s, the government passed the Clean Air Acts to reduce air pollution. In 2007 the government banned smoking in public places.	6 The twentieth century saw many compulsory vaccination campaigns which attempted to eradicate diseases, such as the polio campaign of the 1950s and 1960s.
7 In 1928 Fleming discovered the mould from which the first penicillin was extracted.	8 At the start of the twentieth century doctors were able to identify the specific bacteria causing a range of diseases.	9 By the 1940s Florey and Chain had discovered a way to mass produce penicillin.
10 The NHS was introduced in 1948 as a free service for medical care for everyone. ✓	11 By 1914 the first medical cures had been developed. They were referred to as 'magic bullets' due to the way they worked.	12 Technology such as X-rays and ultrasound scans make it easier for doctors to diagnose illness in patients. ✓
13 Other treatments such as radiotherapy and chemotherapy have proven successful in the treatment of cancer. ✓	14 Dialysis and heart bypass machines can buy a patient time while other treatments and cures are explored. ✓	15 The government now takes a much more proactive role in people's health with campaigns such as 'Stoptober' and 'change4life'. ✓

6 **a** 1 – Genes in the body which are causing disease can be replaced with healthy ones.

2 – People are more likely to 'feel' better as medication will be more effective on the symptoms they are experiencing.

3 – Some organs can be replaced if they fail thus extending the life of a patient who would otherwise die due to an organ no longer functioning.

4 – Doctors therefore have a greater understanding of one particular area and push forward development in their own areas increasing the pace of progress

5 – Helps the health of the public by limiting the harmful effects of 'second-hand smoking'

6 – If as many people as possible are vaccinated the disease cannot spread and eventually can be eradicated – no one has it.

7 – Penicillin can kill just infection and not the patient and was the first 'cure' to infection.

8 – If you can identify the bacteria causing disease you can study their behaviour and try to develop vaccinations and even cures.

9 – This made sure a cure to infection was produced on a scale that could actually save people's lives.

10 – Diagnosis, care, treatments and preventions became available to anyone who needed it.

11 – They could target and kill specific bacteria without killing the patient.

12 – Better diagnosis can lead to more effective (earlier) treatment.

13 – Radiotherapy and chemotherapy kill a number of cells in the body including cancer cells. The hope is that your body can replace cells normally found in the body but cancer cells remain destroyed.

14 – This helps prolong life in cases where no cure or correction is available yet and the patient needs to 'buy some time'.

15 – This is a form of prevention by educating the public on how they might help themselves and live a healthier lifestyle to prevent certain lifestyle-based diseases/ illnesses.

b Will depend on student's answer to **6** **a**:

1 – government, technology, scientific investigation

2 – disease knowledge, technology

3 – technology

4 – disease knowledge, scientific investigation

5 – government, disease knowledge

6 – technology, disease knowledge, scientific investigation, government

7 – disease knowledge, chance, scientific investigation

8 – disease knowledge, technology, scientific investigation

9 – technology, scientific investigation

10 – government

11 – disease knowledge, scientific investigation

12 – technology

13 – disease knowledge, technology

14 – technology

15 – government, disease knowledge

Page 75

1 **a** and **b** Student's own response.

Page 76

1 **a** Student's own response but suggestion:

Measure of significance	A ⊘	Score	B ⊘	Score
Change	✓	5	✓	5
(both saw massive changes)				
Perception	✓	5	✓	5
(both impacted on population - antibiotics on mortality and NHS on access to medicine and treatment (which would have secondary effect on mortality) and both would have been obvious to people at the time)				
Longevity	✓	5	✓	4
(we experience legacy of both still today though current questions on future of NHS)				
Inspiration	✓	5	✓	5
(original discovery of penicillin has led to discovery of different types of antibiotics and preventative medicine; NHS has facilitated research into new treatments and procedures)				
Scale	✓ (global)	5	✓	2 (only valid to UK)
(antibiotics works on a global scale whereas NHS is only really valid to UK)				

b Student's own response but both could get the same number of ticks.

2 **a**, **b** Student's own response but could be:
Antibiotics = 25, NHS = 21

Page 77

1 **2** and **3** Student's own response.

Page 78

1 **a** Ticks

Judgement 1 – A, B,

Judgement 2 – A, B, C, D

Judgement 3 – A, B, D

b Student's own response.

Page 79

1 **2** and **3** Student's own response.

Notes